RISJ *CHALLENGES*

Summoned by Science

Reporting Climate Change at Copenhagen and Beyond

James Painter

REUTERS
INSTITUTE for the
STUDY of
JOURNALISM

UNIVERSITY OF
OXFORD

BRITISH
COUNCIL

Contents

List of Figures

List of Tables in Appendix 2

Foreword by Dr David Viner

Global Director Climate Change and Sustainability, British Council

Copenhagen was the fifteenth step of many that the international community has taken towards reaching a global deal on climate change. The Reuters Institute for the Study of Journalism has shown considerable foresight in tackling the media challenges around the reporting of this issue. This report demonstrates that there is a need for the building of trust and engagement between scientists, media professionals and also policy-makers.

As a scientist who has been involved in the study of climate change for nearly 20 years, I was surprised to be challenged recently by a colleague who suggested that climate change was a topical issue, thus inferring that 'it will go away'. Let me put this into the right context: in the 1860s a British scientist, John Tyndall realised that slight changes in the composition of certain gases in the atmosphere could bring about change in the climate. This was further supported by the Swedish physicist Svante Arrhenius who also realised that emissions of gases as a result of the industrial revolution were likely to be changing the atmosphere and estimated that a doubling of carbon dioxide would lead to a global temperature increase of up to 6 degrees Celsius.

This is remarkably similar to what the most advanced computer models are estimating today. In the 1950s, for the first time we were able to have accurate measurements of the composition of gases in the atmosphere, showing a year on year increase in carbon dioxide concentrations. This was followed by the construction of the global temperature curve by the Climatic Research Unit at the University of East Anglia (where I worked from 1991 to 2007). The Second Assessment Report of the IPCC published in 1995 concluded that 'There is a discernible human influence on the climate system'. So we are dealing with an issue that has been in the scientific consciousness for nearly 150 years and has been in the public's line of sight for nearly 20. The detail of the science is complex, but at the macro level it is simple: the more greenhouses gases in the atmosphere, the warmer the planet. Hardly a topical issue then?

Following on from the way climate change has been reported recently, most notably around hacked emails from the Climatic Research Unit known as 'Climategate', and the even more unfortunately named 'Himalayagate', many scientists no longer trust the media to report fairly and, above all else, accurately on the science of climate change. Scientists are excellent communicators between themselves, but it is how knowledge is disseminated beyond them that is the issue, as they are often not great public communicators. We know that the overwhelming majority of scientists understand climate change as can be seen in the scientific literature. So why is it that media professionals are failing to get this message across or at times deliberately distorting the issue?

There is now an even more urgent requirement for media professionals and journalists to work more closely together in order for journalists to gain a better understanding of the scientific issues and for scientists to understand the requirements of the media. Scientists are accountable to their peers for the quality of their work and rigour behind it, the media are far less so. The trust deficit between the media and scientists is damaging. This is why the British Council has put in place a programme of activity that is bringing scientists and media professionals together to share knowledge and best practice, and also to discuss the variations in the way the issue is reported in different countries. This publication provides the underpinning evidence for our work in this area and one that will help the discourse between climate scientists and media professionals.

Executive Summary

Climate change is a notoriously difficult subject for journalists to report on, for editors to maintain interest in, and for audiences to grasp. The science is complex and incremental, its worst effects are (probably) a long way off, and the topic is now fraught with controversy. Like many slow-burn but hugely urgent issues of the twenty-first century, part of the journalistic challenge remains that of conveying the importance of the science to audiences around the world – in short, 'to make the significant interesting'.

News editors tend to be drawn to events, rather than to slow processes. This was exemplified by the UN's Copenhagen summit on climate change in December 2009. The summit was marked by history, not because it ended in an ambitious and binding deal to curb greenhouse gas emissions but because of the huge number of journalists, delegates, NGOs and scientists present. It is very doubtful that any single event outside of the Olympics or the World Cup has ever attracted so many politicians, journalists, scientists and academics to attend it together.

Around 4,000 journalists from 119 countries were at the summit. 85% of them came from the developed world. But significant numbers also came from the developing world. Nearly 600 journalists from the main negotiating bloc representing the interests of the world's 130 poorest countries – the G-77 plus China – registered to cover the event. China and Brazil were two of the countries most represented by their media, with more than one hundred journalists each.

Historically, the media in most developing countries have not given much priority to climate change, although the amount of coverage has slowly increased in recent years. This is despite the fact that many of these countries are considered the most vulnerable to the impacts of global warming. So Copenhagen represented a rich opportunity for developing-country journalists to change the historic deficit.

With so many journalists present from so many countries, it is hardly surprising that the media coverage of Copenhagen was massive. Most journalists reported extensively on the drama and minutiae of the negotiations. But in the balance between capturing the drama of Copenhagen and explaining the essential background to the science, understandably – but perhaps regrettably – the science was under-reported.

Our analysis of more than 400 articles published in two print media in 12 countries across the world shows that the articles written principally about the science of climate change represented less than 10% of all the articles surveyed. Nearly 80% of the articles mentioned the science in less than 10% of their column space.

Much of the science reporting that there was in the Western press was driven by coverage of the hacked emails from the University of East Anglia in the UK or what the media dubbed 'Climategate'. Climate change sceptics were barely quoted in the articles surveyed, but when they were, it was only in the Western press. This follows a general pattern of very little airtime or print coverage given to sceptics in the media of the developing world.

When the science was reported, it was representatives of international and national bodies (including governments) who were by far the most quoted. Around 2,000 members of delegations from 250 universities were present at Copenhagen, including 280 professors. But scientists from universities represented only 12% of those quoted on the science, compared to 11% for NGOs.

Part of the explanation for this is that NGOs and governments had far more communication officers or media relations personnel at Copenhagen than universities. For example, Greenpeace alone had more media people there than all the universities put together (20 compared to 12). The IPCC has just one paid media officer. Greenpeace had a larger total delegation than that of the UK.

Given that the science of climate change was hardly reported when the peg and the opportunity were self-evident, getting the science into print or onto the airwaves will remain even more of a challenge, demanding a reinvigorated debate about new, interesting and engaging ways to do it. For climate scientists, the issue of how best to engage with the media and public more effectively has also become more urgent because of signs (in the West) of a temporary decline in public confidence in climate science caused partly by 'Climategate' and other publicised errors about the science.

Despite this recent questioning of the robustness of climate science, our survey of more than 50 environment journalists and climate scientists around the world (but with bias towards the UK) suggests that the relationship between the communities is not as bad as many fear. Nearly two-thirds of respondents described the relationship with the other as 'good' or 'very good' (although some would see this as evidence of too 'cosy' a relationship).

The scientists surveyed would like to see the following as the top three priorities to improve the relationship in the coming months: more training for general journalists, more journalists specialising in climate science and a 'less adversarial framing' of climate science (i.e. less space given to sceptics).

The journalists would like to see more reports by climate scientists on topical issues, more availability by scientists to speak to the media, and more scientists who are prepared to debate with climate sceptics. Just behind, in fourth, came more media training for scientists.

As part of the contribution to the debate about the future of climate science reporting, we drew on the surveys and interviews with scientists, journalists and other specialists to come up with eight suggestions or issues to consider for the future. We have chosen three to highlight:

- More of the 'empirical' angle 'what are people experiencing and what are they doing about it?' could replace the ubiquitous reporting (in the Western press) of the adversarial 'Is it happening or not? Are humans to blame? Will the disaster come or not?' Some of the money spent by editors on sending journalists to summits like Copenhagen could be redirected to more investigations of local vulnerabilities and impacts, particularly for journalists in developing countries, and more on what cities, communities and individuals are doing all round the world to switch to low-carbon living.

- However bad the experience of climate scientists at the hands of parts of the media, more of them need to engage or re-engage with journalists in part to explain where there is scientific consensus and where there is not. More training will help, and the Science Media Centre in London is often praised as a model for the future. But there is also a strong case for more dedicated climate change press officers at universities and research centres. The IPCC for its part urgently needs not just a new communications strategy but more resources for press work than the one media officer they currently employ.

- It is a truism that the media landscape in which both journalists and scientists work has been permanently revolutionised by the role of the internet, and particularly the blogosphere. More use of social media will be crucial for engagement, participation and trust rather than top–down information. New media offer excellent opportunities for frontline citizen journalism and video reporting, more dialogue with sceptics and the public, and data collection and sharing.

1. Introduction

The UN's Copenhagen summit on climate change in December 2009 has been variously described as a tragedy, a farce or a step in the right direction. But whatever the correct verdict, it is one of the few times that the use of the adjective 'historic' can be fully justified. It was unprecedented that around 120 heads of state were summoned to a meeting by the science. Never before had so many journalists from so many different countries come to the same place to cover an event that wasn't the World Cup or the Olympics. And – perhaps the least reported fact of all – it would be hard to find a political event which attracted so many hundreds of scientists and students from universities and research centres around the world.

A staggering 3,880 journalists from 119 countries were registered to attend the Copenhagen summit, or COP-15 (the fifteenth Conference of the Parties) to give it its official title. Of these, about 3,220 actually received badges of accreditation. In part this was due to several journalists being unable to enter the conference hall: the giant, hanger-like Bella centre had had a limit imposed on it because the thousands trying to get in far outnumbered its capacity. After queuing outside for hours in what were at times sub-zero temperatures, several journalists were to be forgiven for giving up on ever joining the party.

However, as we shall argue in Chapter 3, if you add the hundreds of journalists accompanying their heads of state and the dozens of journalists who registered on other UN lists, then it would be no exaggeration to say that there were around 4,000 occupants of the Bella centre engaged in writing or broadcasting about the summit. The first great green event, the Rio Summit in 1992, attracted about 1,000 press and TV journalists. At the next seminal climate change event in Kyoto in 1997 about 3,700 turned up, but this number was swollen by large numbers of Japanese TV technicians.

Moreover, it was the first time at a climate change conference that journalists from developing countries were out in force. As we will see in Chapter 3, nearly 600 journalists from the main negotiating bloc representing the interests of the world's 130 poorest countries – the G-77 plus China – were registered for the event. They had come from 68 countries. Normally the high costs of attending such events are prohibitive. But this time 29 (more than half) of Africa's 54 countries were represented, as many of their journalists had been funded by NGOs, Western governments and UN bodies. Brazil and China, two of the four emerging powerhouse countries known as the BRIC (the other two being Russia and India), had more than 100 journalists each at Copenhagen, and probably half as many again if the journalists travelling with their heads of state are included.

India and Bangladesh had more media representatives registered than Russia and South Korea; China and Brazil more than Italy, Spain and Australia. At the very least, the numbers suggest a re-evaluation of the widely held view that news consumers in the countries most vulnerable to the impacts of climate change always suffer an information deficit and have to depend on Western news agencies.

Copenhagen was also one of the largest political events covered by new media, such as the internet, blogs and tweeters. More than 240 journalists registered as online journalists – a record number for COPs and nearly five times the number for the summit in Bali two years previously. Google alone had 27 journalists registered. A timeline on Google News showed the very large number of sources covering the summit.[1] On Twitter, the amount of tweets from and about the event was huge. The traffic reached 13,000 tweets even before the climax of the negotiations in the last couple of days.[2] As one observer put it, Copenhagen was 'the broadest *simultaneous* [my emphasis] coverage of climate change in world history'.[3]

The vast majority of journalists did not travel to Copenhagen to report the science. Their main focus was naturally on whether the 190-plus countries represented there could agree on some sort of a deal to curb greenhouse gas emissions (GHGs) and avoid further anthropogenic climate change in the future. As it turned out, they were given layer upon layer of richly fertile material as the negotiations offered a compelling narrative of textual warfare, threatened walkouts, geopolitical bad-mouthing, brinkmanship, a weak accord announced first to the White House press corps, and finally, fierce recriminations.[4] In the words of the British novelist Ian McEwan, there was enough happening at Copenhagen 'to furnish a novel'. Even though old hacks admitted that most of the time they had little idea of exactly what was going

---

[1] Curtis Brainard and Cristine Russell, 'Copenhagen Watch: Bipolar Coverage Disorder?', *The Observatory: Columbia Journalism Review* (16 Dec. 2009)

[2] Ibid.

[3] Ben Block, 'Covering Climate Change', *World Watch* (March/April 2010).

[4] A flavour of what Copenhagen was like for a reporter can be found in the Epilogue of the book written by the BBC environment correspondent David Shukman, *Reporting Live from the End of the World* (London: Profile Books, 2010).

on,[5] the drama could hardly have been more engaging.

However, although the 'story' from Copenhagen was essentially about policy and the cut and thrust of the negotiations, the science of climate change formed the essential backdrop for understanding and explaining why the negotiations were so vital. The tabloid *Daily Express* in the UK clearly saw the link when it splashed across its pages on 15 December the headline '100 Reasons Why Global Warming is Natural' based on a report by 'political analyst Jim McConalogue' at the 'respected' European Foundation. McConalogue was quoted as saying that Copenhagen was likely to lead to 'nonsensical targets'.[6] The *New Scientist* magazine gave up debunking the 100 'reasons' after the first 50, as most were very questionable science.[7]

A more science-based series of reports than McConalogue's released in the months running up to Copenhagen suggested something quite different: the need for an ambitious and binding deal was made all the more urgent by the latest science. For example, in September 2009 the United Nations Environment Programme (UNEP) published peer-reviewed literature showing that 'the pace and scale of climate change may now be outstripping even the most sobering predictions of the IPCC'[8] – a reference to the seminal series of reports released by the IPCC (Intergovernmental Panel on Climate Change) in 2007 which are based on consensus and seen by many scientists as conservative. In September a conference packed full of scientists and hosted at the Environmental Change Institute (ECI) at Oxford University warned soberly of the possible consequences of a four-degree rise in global temperatures at some point this century.[9]

On the very eve of Copenhagen, the IPCC was at pains to stress the importance of the science. Its chairman, Dr Rajendra K. Pachauri, said simply in a video address to delegates at the pre-Copenhagen negotiating meeting in November in Barcelona that 'the time has come for us to return to the science of climate change'. The co-chair of the IPCC's Working Group 1, Professor Thomas Stocker, made a similar point at Barcelona when he stressed that continued GHG emissions would induce many changes very likely larger than those already observed, and that there were unprecedented changes in the climate system in both amplitude and rate. As *Science* magazine reported on 13 November, 'almost all climate scientists are of one mind about the threat

[5] Richard Black, 'COP15 Copenhagen Climate Summit: Day 4', BBC website, 10 Dec. 2009: www.bbc.co.uk/blogs/thereporters/richardblack/2009/12/cop15_copenhagen_climate_summi_2.html.
[6] Martyn Brown, '100 Reasons Why Global Warming is Natural', *Daily Express* (15 Dec. 2009): www.dailyexpress.co.uk/posts/view/146139.
[7] This can be found at www.newscientist.com/blogs/shortsharpscience/2009/12/50-reasons-why-global-warming.html.
[8] UNEP press release on 24 Sept. 2009: www.unep.org/compendium2009/.
[9] The details of the conference can be found at www.eci.ox.ac.uk/4degrees/index.php. The UK Met Office maps showing the impacts of a 2C and 4C temperature rise can be found at: www.metoffice.gov.uk/corporate/pressoffice/2009/pr20091022.html

of global warming: It's real, it's dangerous and the world needs to take action immediately.'[10]

So it was not just the heads of state, but journalists too who had been summoned to Copenhagen by the urgency of the climate science. The summit offered a remarkable opportunity for media organisations to include in their coverage an explanation to their readers or viewers the essential background for understanding why this is so. Editors back home were happy to grant column inches and broadcast time to the issue of climate change like never before. In some newspapers included in this study they did just that, but in others they did not. Moreover, even though the negotiations were the top story, as will be shown in Chapter 4, a considerable amount of 'new' science released during the two weeks of the summit could have been reported.

Another compelling reason for expecting some coverage of the science was the presence of hundreds of scientists at Copenhagen. As we shall see in Chapter 3, official lists of those who made it to the Bella Centre suggest that there were around 2,000 members of the delegations from nearly 250 universities all around the world. Hundreds more scientists were present from research centres, academic associations and science and technology centres. No less than 280 professors were present. Even though many of those were scientists from different disciplines to climate science or students not yet able or willing to engage with the media, it is reasonable to conclude that there were dozens of experts in the various branches of climate science on hand in Copenhagen.

In this study, we have examined the media coverage of the summit across six days in 12 different countries to address three essential questions. How much did the science of climate change get reported in these countries? When the science was discussed in the media, who got quoted on the science – politicians, NGOs or scientists? And whose reactions were most sought to the accord signed at the end of the summit by Brazil, USA, South Africa, India and China?

The 12 countries chosen were Australia, Brazil, China, Egypt, India, Italy, Mexico, Nigeria, Russia, United Kingdom, USA, and Vietnam. The aim was to have a rich mix of the developed and developing worlds, with particular emphasis on major emerging economies with a powerful voice in the negotiations (Brazil, China, India and Mexico). It was also of particular interest that seven of these countries were from the developing world. As will be seen in Chapter 2, the vast majority of academic studies based on content analysis of climate change coverage have tended to concentrate on the media in the (usually English-speaking) industrialised world. Moreover, it is only in

---

[10] Richard A. Kerr, 'Climate Change: Amid Worrisome Signs of Warming, "Climate Fatigue" Sets in', *Science* (13 Nov. 2009).

recent years that coverage of climate change has increased from a low base in many developing countries. Again, Copenhagen offered a marvellous peg to correct the historic deficit.

Eight of the case studies either include or are totally focused on print or online media in the vernacular. These newspapers tend to have a far greater reach than English-language media in these countries. A total of more than 420 articles were analysed. To complement the content analysis, we drew on research papers written by RISJ journalist fellows over the last three years and a series of seminars and events held jointly by the RISJ, the OUCE and the ECI at Oxford University.[11] For several years M.Sc. students at the ECI and RISJ fellows have held joint seminars to try and jointly understand the different drivers of media coverage and the public dissemination of science. In particular, a series of events in February 2010 on the reporting of climate science at Copenhagen and beyond generated a substantial input into this publication.[12]

One of the main conclusions from our research is that, despite their large numbers at Copenhagen, scientists from universities and research centres were quoted much less on the science compared to other sectors, and only on three occasions more than NGOs. As argued in Chapter 5, there are reasons which explain why this could have happened. One of them is the climate of intimidation created by online bloggers and others against climate scientists, particularly before, during and after the media uproar over the hacking of large numbers of emails from the Climatic Research Unit (CRU) at the University of East Anglia, some of which were quoted by sceptics as evidence that climate scientists had changed their results to make global warming appear worse than it is.[13] We shall discuss the effect of what the media inevitably dubbed 'Climategate' more fully in Chapter 6. But it is clear that some scientists simply chose to keep their heads down.

The Copenhagen summit took place at a time when opinion polls, at least in the USA, the UK and some other countries of Europe, appeared to show that even though the science of climate change was becoming more certain, the public were becoming more sceptical about the science underpinning it. This has prompted more debate about the nature of climate change reporting in the media and the obstacles to better public understanding.

Some of the media's readiness to give more of a voice to climate change

[11] See e.g. 'Carbonundrums: Making Sense of Climate Change Reporting around the World', held on 27 June 2007, details available at www.eci.ox.ac.uk/news/events/070727-carbonundrum/index.php.
[12] The last three years have focused on the reporting of the science of climate change during the Bali, Poznan and Copenhagen summits in countries where the journalists and M.Sc. students were from. For the Feb. 2010 events, see http://reutersinstitute.politics.ox.ac.uk/about/news/item/article/making-waves-reporting-climate-cha.html.
[13] The amount of words written on 'Climategate' is already extensive. A good place to start is Fred Pearce's book, *The Climate Files* (London: Guardian Books, 2010), although it has been criticised by some for creating too much of a scandal when there wasn't one to report.

sceptics (after a period of relative silence), the rise in the climate-sceptic blogosphere, the extensive coverage of 'Climategate' and of errors in the IPCC reports form part of the background.[14] But age-old obstacles to understanding climate change and to the media's accurate reporting of it persist: the science is difficult, complex and at times uncertain; the public confuse the weather with the climate; the media are attracted to contrarian views, even though they may be unrepresentative; climate change fatigue easily sets in; in the public's eyes, established views can get mixed up with establishment views.

At least in the UK and the USA, there is a vibrant debate taking place as to what might constitute different or better reporting by the mainstream media, and how the climate science community should re-engage with them and the public. It was in the spirit of trying to contribute to this urgent debate both in the UK and internationally that we sent out short questionnaires to several environmental journalists and climate scientists in the 12 countries whose media we surveyed, receiving responses from 27 journalists and 27 climate scientists.

The results described in Chapter 6 give a snapshot – it can be no more than that – of the relationship between the two communities. They include what each group thinks the other should make priorities for the future, and ideas that have worked well in individual countries. So we draw on these initiatives, the conclusions of our research and other interviews to end with a rather eclectic and modest list of eight ideas that could help surmount what many see as a crisis both in public confidence in climate science and in reporting what is one of the most pressing issues of our age.

---

[14] For one of the most detailed discussions of the IPCC's main error about the Himalayan glaciers, see www.climatesciencewatch.org/index.php/csw/details/ipcc_slips_on_the_ice; and for a general discussion of the IPCC's shortcomings, see Pearce, *Climate Files*, ch. 16.

2. Trends and issues in international climate change coverage

Introduction

Most academic studies of the media coverage of climate change in recent years have concentrated almost exclusively on newspapers. This is regrettable as the majority of people in many countries of the world say their most popular source of news is television. For example, even with the high internet usage in the USA, although Americans increasingly use multiple sources of news information, they turn to local television news and national or cable television news more than the internet as their main source.[15] In the UK, the independent regulator Ofcom found in 2010 that audiences for flagship TV news programmes have generally held up since 2004 despite the greater access to other news sources, and remain the main source of news for most of the British population.[16] Reliance on TV for news is even more the case for most developing countries due to the widespread access to TV sets, low reach of newspapers (particularly in rural areas) and lower literacy rates (Appendix 1).[17]

Moreover, there is evidence to suggest that national television is not just the most used but the most *trusted* source of news in most countries by some distance, when compared to newspapers, news websites, radio and blogs.[18] But there are several practical obstacles to including TV broadcasts in any content

[15] Kristen Purcell, Lee Rainie, Amy Mitchell, Tom Rosenstiel, Kenny Olmstead, 'Understanding the Participatory News Consumer', Pew Internet and American Life Project, 1 March 2010.
[16] The country's most popular news programme, *BBC News at Ten*, had an average daily audience of 4.7 million in 2009. Oliver Luft, 'Ofcom: Audience Fightback for Flagship News Programmes', *Press Gazette* (1 July 2010).
[17] The exception to this general trend is Africa, where despite the advance of the internet and particularly mobile phones, radio is still the most dominant medium for receipt of news in many countries. See the BBC media profiles for all countries, available at news.bbc.co.uk/1/hi/country_profiles/default.stm.
[18] See Appendix 1 for sources.

13

analysis. It is immensely time-consuming to watch television broadcasts or listen to radio programmes compared to processing print and online media. It is also difficult to physically get hold of recordings of the programmes in sufficient quantities to make the sample robust.

As will be seen in Chapter 4, we too have reluctantly concentrated on print media because of the time constraints and the practical difficulties of monitoring TV channels in 12 different countries. It is particularly to be regretted because television journalists were by far the largest media category present at Copenhagen. But we do agree with the arguments that print media have a strong agenda-setting influence on policy-makers and other elites, and in many media landscapes act as 'gatekeepers of information' and prompts for coverage in the other media, including TV and radio.[19]

The second regrettable aspect of media analysis of climate change over the last two decades has been its focus on the print media in English-speaking countries, and particularly the USA and the UK, or on English-language newspapers in developing countries which tend to have much lower reach than their vernacular equivalents. As one Peruvian scholar recently observed:[20]

> Research on mass media coverage and public opinion of
> climate change is abundant in the literature, but these studies
> focus mostly on developed countries (especially the US), with
> limited understanding of how the issue is being reported and
> perceived in developing countries, many of which are more
> vulnerable to the effects of climate change.

The research focus on developed rather than developing countries is obviously problematic. As the IPCC reports have pointed out, it is the poorest countries in the world and the poorest sectors within them who are most likely to be affected first by climate change. But it is they who have contributed the least GHG emissions. Sub-Saharan African countries are particularly at risk, and Africans are in general the 'least responsible, most affected and least informed', as a recent policy briefing by the BBC World Service Trust has highlighted.[21]

One consequence of the paucity of research is that we do not know enough about how the voices of those who should be some of the most heard in the climate negotiations are represented in their local media, if at all. If no

---

[19] Max Boykoff, 'Indian Media Representations of Climate Change in a Threatened Journalistic Ecosystem', *Climatic Change,* 99 (2010), 17–25, 18. Indian TV journalists are not alone in saying their news agenda is often driven by newspaper stories.

[20] Bruno Takahashi, 'Framing and Sources: A Study of Mass Media Coverage of Climate Change in Peru during the VALCUE', *Public Understanding of Science,* 1 (2010), 1–15.

[21] BBC World Service Trust, 'Least Responsible, Most Affected, Least Informed: Public Understanding of Climate Change in Africa', *Policy Briefing,* 3 (Oct. 2009): http://downloads.bbc.co.uk/worldservice/pdf/wstrust/PB_climatechange_web.pdf.

information – or the wrong sort – is reaching those most at risk from climate change, how can they be expected to adapt to climate change or hold to account their own or Western governments and negotiators? And it is difficult to identify what would improve media coverage and public awareness in developing countries if we do not have enough information about how the issue is framed, what angles get covered, what prompts coverage, what sources journalists rely on and which sectors get quoted.

However, it should be stressed that the situation is slowly improving as more media scholars are carrying out content analysis of developing countries and non-English-language media in industrialised countries.[22] India, China and Latin America in particular are all receiving more attention.[23] Multiple-country comparative studies of the amount and type of media coverage are also now appearing, and are immensely valuable in beginning to fill the gaps in the literature.[24] This study is intended to help to redress the balance and to contribute to this healthy trend of more comparative studies and more studies of non-English media. It is fortunate to be able draw on the long tradition of comparative international media perspectives encouraged on the RISJ journalism fellowship programme and M.Sc. courses at the ECI and OUCE.

Tracking the coverage

The most valuable exercise in tracking international media coverage is by Dr Max Boykoff and Maria Mansfield, who have been assessing the monthly amount of coverage of climate change or global warming in 50 countries around the world since January 2004. Their results up until September 2010 can be seen in Figure 2.1.

As the authors themselves explain, the figure is more useful for monitoring the historical peaks and troughs of coverage than any comparisons between the volume of stories in each region. This is because the newspapers selected for monitoring are not distributed evenly across the five regions and are mostly English-language. They are however, newspapers which enjoy good

---

[22] See e.g. Astrid Dirikx and Dave Gelders, 'Global Warming through the Same Lens: An Explorative Framing Study in Dutch and French Newspapers', in T. Boyce and J. Lewis (eds), *Climate Change and the Media* (2009); on Japan, see Yuki Sampei and Midori Aoyagi-Usui, 'Mass-Media Coverage, its Influence on Public Awareness of Climate-Change Issues, and Implications for Japan's National Campaign to Reduce Greenhouse Gas Emissions', *Global Environmental Change*, 19/2 (2009): 203–12.
[23] E.g. on India, see S. Billett, 'Dividing Climate Change: Global Warming in the Indian Mass Media', *Climatic Change*, 99/1–2 (March 2010): 1–16; on China, Yan Wu, 'The Good, the Bad, and the Ugly: Framing of China in News Media Coverage of Global Climate Change', in Boyce and Lewis (eds), *Climate Change and the Media*; and on Peru, Takahashi, 'Framing and Sources'.
[24] P. Coulter and A. Midttun (eds), 'Escaping Climate Change: Climate Change in the Media: North and South Perspectives', CERES, June 2009: www.ceres21.org/webcontrol/UploadedDocuments/Ceres21%20 Escaping%20Climate%20Change.pdf; Elisabeth Eide, Risto Kunelius and Ville Kumpu, 'Domesticating a Global Moment: Transnational Study on the Coverage of Bali and Copenhagen Climate Summits', paper presented at the IAMCR, Braga, July 2010.

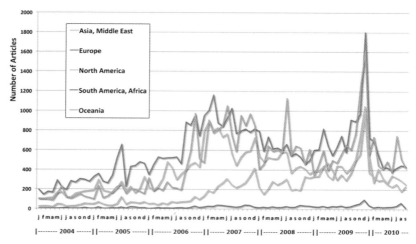

© Maxwell Boykoff, Centre for Science and Technology Policy Research, University of Colorado and Maria Mansfield, ECI, Oxford University

Figure 2.1. 2004–2010 world newspaper coverage of climate change or global warming

circulation and widespread influence over policy-makers.[25]

As can be seen from the figure, the coverage in different parts of the world reached a peak in 2007 before peaking again massively at the end of 2009 which coincided with the Copenhagen summit – a theme we shall return to in Chapter 4. 2007 was the year of the last IPCC reports, the wide dissemination of Al Gore's film *An Inconvenient Truth* and the holding of the UN's climate change summit in Bali in December 2007. The graph suggests a dramatic decline in the early part of 2010 (after the Copenhagen summit) in all regions to early 2006 levels, but history suggests that it will pick up again.

Although you cannot extrapolate from the figure that print coverage of climate change is generally far higher in Europe, North America and Oceania than in Asia, the Middle East, South America and Africa, it would be very surprising if this was not the case. In his definitive overview of the state of media reporting in developing countries, Mike Shanahan from the International Institute for Environment and Development (IIED) paints a depressing picture of the obstacles to more or better media coverage in 12 developing countries.[26] He concludes that despite some evidence for climate

[25] Only three are from South America and Africa, compared to 11 just from the UK. Only one (*Clarín* in Argentina) is not in English. The full list of papers and discussion by the authors can be found at http://sciencepolicy.colorado.edu/media_coverage.
[26] Mike Shanahan, 'Time to Adapt? Media Coverage of Climate Change in Non-Industrialised Countries', in Boyce and Lewis (eds), *Climate Change and the Media*, ch. 12.

change rising up the media agenda in developing countries in 2008, 'the quantity and quality of reporting do not match the scale of the problem'. In particular Shanahan bemoans the reliance on Western news agencies rather than more locally relevant news.

Recent studies would suggest that in some countries where low levels of reporting have historically been the case, it may now be changing. In China and India – obviously the two giant booming economies of Asia, but also the world's first and fourth largest gross emitters of GHGs – there are signs that the amount of coverage has been increasing in the last couple of years. In India, English-language national newspaper coverage of climate change or global warming rose strongly between mid-2008 and the end of 2009.[27] Unfortunately we do not know the trends in Hindi-language newspapers or TV coverage which enjoy a much wider reach, although anecdotal evidence would suggest that there is still significantly less coverage in these two genres.[28]

In China, one 2009 study suggested that the amount of coverage in some Chinese media shot up in 2007 after very low coverage from 1998 to 2006 (49 stories compared to 24 in the whole of the previous period), although it declined again in 2008. The author of the study argued that the increase was 'primarily an attempt by the Communist government to be seen to respond to the global finger-pointing at China's CO2 emissions'.[29] Similarly, research by RISJ journalist fellow Christina Larson in 2009 suggested that, from a low base in 2006, climate change coverage has risen due to a series of factors including the announcement of China's first national climate change programme in 2007 to the widespread snow storms and unusually low temperatures in early 2008.[30] According to her research, a major impetus was given in 2008 when the Chinese State Council released a policy document, *China's Policies and Actions for Addressing Climate Change*, which laid out official positions and called for more coverage about climate change in the state-run media.

There is strong evidence to suggest that the Chinese authorities now allow, or even encourage, coverage of climate change and the environment compared to other topics. As John Wihbey has written,[31] 'Democracy, Tiananmen Square, Tibet, Falun Gong, and other sensitive topics still seem off-limits. But not the environment or climate. On those topics, there is ongoing coverage in the state-backed *China Daily* newspaper and on the media giant CCTV.'

There have been few studies of the media coverage of climate change in Latin America which map the changing trends. However, there is some evidence for

[27] Boykoff, 'Indian Media Representations', fig. 2.
[28] Comments made by Indian journalists at the Feb. 2010 RISJ/ECI seminars.
[29] Yan Wu, 'The Good, the Bad, and the Ugly', p. 162.
[30] Christina Larson, 'Coverage of Climate Change in the Chinese Media', presentation at the RISJ, Oxford, June 2009.
[31] John Wihbey, 'China's Climate "Free" Media in the International Spotlight', Yale Forum on Climate Change and the Media, 23 Feb. 2010: www.yaleclimatemediaforum.org/2010/02/chinas-climate-free-media.

thinking that coverage in Brazil began to take off in the last half of 2006.[32] The relationship between the amount of media coverage and public awareness in a particular country is never straightforward. However, Brazil often emerges as having one of the highest levels of awareness and concern of any country in the world.[33] There are many reasons which contribute to this being the case: the Amazon on the doorstep, the political and economic elite taking the issue seriously, a strong environmental NGO sector, and a body of eminent Brazilian climate change scientists. But it is also true that the Brazilian media now dedicate a larger amount of coverage to the theme than the media in other countries. It is a trend corroborated by our study of Copenhagen which we will discuss further in Chapter 4.

Outside of Brazil, there is some evidence to suggest that the amount of coverage is increasing in other South American countries too.[34] But it is from a very low base, as shown by one of the few comparative studies of South American print media carried out by the Konrad Adenauer Institute in Buenos Aires in April 2008. After examining the two most read newspapers in seven South American countries, the study concluded that of 4,000 articles examined in detail over a period of a month from January to February 2008, only about 10–20 of them mentioned the theme of climate change. It very seldom appeared as a headline, and when it was covered, it was often framed as an international problem with little mention of the local consequences. The study is restricted by the short period of time examined and so is not helpful for exploring trends. However, recent research done on Peru would suggest a notable increase in the amount of coverage in two of the country's leading newspapers between 2004 and 2009. Of the 426 articles surveyed, all but 23 were from the more recent period of 2007 to 2009.[35]

Africa too suffers from a paucity of comparative or individual studies of its media coverage of climate change, despite its extreme vulnerability to present and future changes in the climate. One exception is a 2009 study comparing

---

[32] A study funded by the British embassy in Brasilia and carried out in 2008 by an NGO called ANDI found that between the last quarter of 2006 and mid-2007, 50 key Brazilian daily newspapers registered a steep rise in the amount of space given to climate change (although updated research showed that there was a decline in the second half of 2007 which extended into 2008, but not back to the end of 2005/beginning of 2006 levels). See ANDI, 'Climate Change in the Brazilian Press: A Comparative Analysis of 50 Newspapers from July 2005 to June 2007, July 2007 to December 2008'. A similar story was found by a Brazilian RISJ journalist fellow, Carlos Fioravanti, who detected a four-fold increase in *Folha de Sao Paulo* between the second half of 2006 and first half of 2007.

[33] For example, a BBC World Service/Globescan poll in Dec. 2009, which drew on interviews with 24,000 adults in 23 countries, placed Brazil joint top (with Chile) as the country with the highest percentage of interviewees who saw climate change as a 'very serious' problem (86%). Similarly, a survey of nine countries by HSBC in 2007 suggested that climate change was the number one concern in Brazil by a bigger margin than in any other country.

[34] James Painter, 'Climate Change, Latin America and the Media', annual lecture to the Society of Latin American Studies, 7 Nov. 2008, pp. 6 ff.: www.slas.org.uk/events.htm#anLec.

[35] Daniel Waite, 'Apathy in the Andes: Exploring the Dominant Discourses in Peruvian Media Coverage of Climate Change', unpublished MA thesis, Oxford University, 2010.

the amount of coverage of climate change from January to June 2008 in Ghana, China and Norway. Ghana lagged far behind the other two countries.[36]

The scant coverage in the Nigerian and South African press has been documented by a Nigerian RISJ journalist fellow, Evelyn Tagbo, in her 2010 research paper 'Media Coverage of Climate Change in African Media'.[37] She monitored the amount of coverage in two Nigerian newspapers (the *Guardian* and *Vanguard*) and in two South African newspapers (the *Star* and the *Mail and Guardian*) in two three-month periods from January to March in 2009 and 2010. In Nigeria, the two papers published 79 articles on climate change, equivalent to less than 0.1% of the total number of articles published on the online sites of the two newspapers during that period. Likewise, the two South African newspapers published slightly more (96), but this still only represented 0.3% of the total number of articles.

A similar picture was revealed by another RISJ journalist fellow, this time from the Pacific island of Samoa – another part of the world like Sub-Saharan Africa where communities face the greatest climate-related risks, yet typically receive little information through the mass media in their countries. Samoa is very vulnerable to sea-level rises, tropical cyclones, temperature rises and shifts in the timing of the wet and dry seasons. In her research, Cherelle Jackson found that of the 1,394 articles published by three Samoan newspapers in the period from May 2008 to May 2009, just 16 were about climate change.[38] This was the smallest number by far of the eight categories she used to distinguish the subject matter of each article, and compared to 643 about business and politics. 'Society coverage', such as weddings and birthdays, featured much more prominently with 186 stories.

The study also found that the UK *Guardian* had almost as much coverage of the precarious situation facing the Pacific Islands in the same period of analysis – 15 articles compared to the 16 in the Samoan press. The editors Jackson interviewed did recognise the importance of the climate change story. But on one occasion Jackson was told by her editor-in-chief that the newspaper did not want to 'alarm people' with climate change stories.

This overview of recent research into climate change coverage in developing countries shows a varied and changing picture. As might be expected, 'the developing world' masks a multitude of different experiences. A gap seems to be emerging between less developed countries and the powerful developing giants like Brazil, India and China, where there is evidence – at least in the print media – to suggest an underlying upwards trend from 2006 until

---

[36] Coulter and Midttun (eds), 'Escaping Climate Change', p. 51.
[37] Evelyn Tagbo, 'Media Coverage of Climate Change in Africa: A Case Study of Nigeria and South Africa', RISJ fellowship paper, Hilary and Trinity terms 2010, forthcoming.
[38] Cherelle Jackson, 'Staying Afloat in Paradise: Reporting Climate Change in the Pacific', RISJ fellowship paper, Hilary term 2010, available from the RISJ website.

Copenhagen in December 2009. In many poorer countries, the amount of coverage remains woefully inadequate and insufficient to match either the scale of the problem or the degree of vulnerability.

Obstacles to more, or better, reporting

The obstacles to more, or better, reporting vary from country to country in the developing world. Nevertheless, Mike Shanahan identified some common themes in his talk to the RISJ/ECI seminar in February 2010. These were:

1. *Lack of training for journalists to make climate change relevant and interesting:* climate change is an immense topic, often feels remote, and involves complex jargon and difficult concepts to describe like risk and uncertainty.

2. *Lack of access to specialist knowledge* in some developing countries. Much of the science is Western and written in English. Many local scientists lack awareness of media needs such as clarity and brevity, whilst government officials who are specialists on climate change are often unavailable.

3. *Lack of resources to travel* outside city centres to garner first-hand evidence and testimony or to attend international climate conferences.

4. *Lack of research available on the country-specific current and future impacts* of climate change.

5. *Too cosy a relationship* between the media and national political leaders, which can lead to an unquestioning attitude of the powers-that-be or an over-willingness to blame the West for global warming.

6. *Unsympathetic editors* who do not see the importance of the story compared to other more pressing or popular concerns.[39]

To the six obstacles listed above, a seventh should be added. Editors and journalists often admit that climate change gets pigeon-holed or dismissed

---

[39] These obstacles resonate with the experience of two RISJ journalist fellows. Cherelle Jackson from Samoa highlighted the 'complexity of the issue, under-resourced newsrooms and accessibility to sources and information on the islands'. Evelyn Tagbo from Nigeria pointed to the use of foreign reports, mostly from international wire services, as a major obstacle. She writes that 'the use of foreign reports, even though they have helped to keep climate change in the news in most African countries, has meant that little of the real situation on ground is reported'. She also found that 60% of the journalists and the editors she interviewed identified lack of training and time pressures as major reasons why climate change has rarely generated coverage commensurate with its significance for Africa's future prosperity.

as an 'environment story', when it has huge implications for energy policy, food security, water supplies, economic development, poverty alleviation, health spending, international relations, technological initiatives, internal and foreign migration, and security issues – to name but a few.

There are of course important variations between countries even within the same region. Dalia Abdel-Salam, environment editor at *Al Ahram Hebdo* in Cairo, told a meeting of the American Association for the Advancement of Science in February 2010 of the problems confronting her colleagues in the Middle East and Africa.[40] Based on an informal poll of her colleagues, she found that:

- climate change stories get short shrift in *Ethiopia* as they are not thought to be 'sexy';

- a lack of interest among top editors and readers as well as a lack of trust in *Malawi* among journalists and government organisations with data;

- a lack of climate-change education and experts in *Tanzania*;

- a lack of national and regional data and uncooperative sources in *Egypt*;

- a lack of sources, resources and information in the Arabic language in *Morocco* and the *United Arab Emirates*.

In some countries reporting on the environment, including climate change-related topics, can also be a threat to life and limb. Reporters Without Borders and 13 other press freedom organisations warned during the Copenhagen summit that 'more and more journalists are nowadays being killed, imprisoned, harassed, censored or intimidated because of their coverage of environmental issues'.[41] Covering illegal logging or pollution can be as dangerous as covering the crime beat in some South East Asian countries. The organisations made the point that, if governments like those in Uzbekistan, Russia, China, Burma or Indonesia did not respect the right of their media to inform on environmental issues, how could they be expected 'to really commit to fight against climate change'?

[40] Robin Lloyd and Christine Russell, 'Better Communication Begets Trust: Experts Press for Localizing Climate Coverage', *The Observatory: Columbia Journalism Review* (23 Feb. 2010).
[41] Reporters Without Borders, 'Call to Action to Protect Environmental Journalists', 11 Dec. 2009: http://en.rsf.org/call-to-action-to-protect-11-12-2009,35315.html.

present, or at least were mitigated, during the Copenhagen summit. As we shall see in the next chapter, editors in most countries subscribed to the view that Copenhagen was the meeting that would decide the fate of the planet. The result was that journalists from developed and developing countries were present in vast numbers, as were large numbers of specialist scientists. The historic lack of coverage of climate change in the media of many developing countries had the potential at least of being corrected in one single event. If getting climate science into the media needs a hook, then this was surely it. At least three of the obstacles to more reporting from developing countries (lack of resources to travel, lack of access to specialist knowledge and unsympathetic editors) were overcome. But as we shall see in Chapter 4, most journalists – understandably but perhaps regrettably – seem to have opted to under-report the science.

3. Who was at Copenhagen?

Anyone arriving at the Bella Centre on the morning of the Monday of the second week of the Copenhagen summit could have been in no doubt that they were witnessing a defining moment in the history of the planet. Even at 8 am the queues of delegates, NGOs and journalists wound their way several hundred yards from the entry doors. What they could not have known was that most of them would have been still queuing in freezing conditions until 5 pm that night. Some reached their personal tipping point and gave up, complaining that global warming had not reached Scandinavia. A frustrated TV crew from the Indian channel NDTV was forced to interview members of the queue, as it was the only story they could report on.[48]

But it wasn't just the media who were stuck outside. A lead author of the 2007 IPCC reports, a head of an official delegation and a chief campaigner from a British NGO were all spotted in the queue. A limit had had to be set by the UNFCCC and the Danish hosts on the huge numbers attracted by the summit. The capacity of the Bella Centre was designed to be 15,000, yet more than 30,000 people had been allowed to pre-register and several hundred more after the start of the summit.[49] Accreditations for journalists had to be capped at 3,500 several days into the summit due to the excessive demand. The long queues were symbolic of the huge interest generated by Copenhagen, or 'Hopenhagen' as it came to be known in the early days. Commissioning editors around the world had bought into the idea that the fate of the planet was in the balance, and that governments might be able to achieve a global contract to reduce carbon emissions in order to save it.

Other summits had attracted thousands of journalists – but not quite like Copenhagen. As Figure 3.1 shows, Copenhagen (COP-15) had a far larger number of journalists – 3,221 – than other COP meetings, with the exception

---

[48] James Painter, 'A la espera del calentamiento global', bbcmundo, 18 Dec. 2009:
www.bbc.co.uk/mundo/ciencia_tecnologia/2009/12/091214_1600_copenhague_painter_sao.shtml.
[49] The official UNFCCC numbers on 8 Dec. for pre-registered attendees were 8,053 delegates, 22,070 observers (mostly NGOs) and 2,941 journalists.

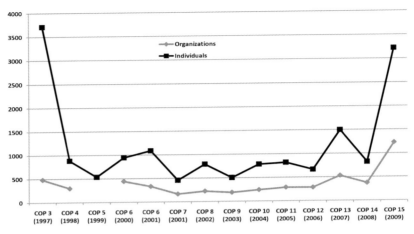

Figure 3.1. Number of journalists and media organisations at COP meetings, 1997 to 2009

of Kyoto (COP-3) in 1997. However, the 3,712 at Kyoto were swollen by the very large number of TV technicians, particularly from the host nation Japan, who were required by the more labour-intensive technology of the day.[50] Moreover, there were at least 500 more journalists, and probably as many as 700, allowed into the Bella Centre to accompany their heads of state. Another 100-odd journalists, particularly working for state media organisations, also appeared on other UN lists (for example, under government delegations or NGOs). So a best guess would be that there were around 4,000 journalists actually in the Bella Centre at some point working for media outlets. It is also worth stressing that Copenhagen saw by the far the largest number of media organisations present at any COP meeting: 1,227 compared to the next largest (531) at Bali in 2007.

It is hard to think of an international event which had ever attracted so much press interest. The World Cup and the Olympics are the obvious exceptions: the 2006 football World Cup brought more than 18,000 media representatives to Germany, 13,000 of whom were TV commentators, technicians or cameramen and 'only' 4,250 were journalists. But these are sporting events. The nearest point of comparison is the US elections in 2008 which may have attracted more journalists cumulatively, but it is doubtful there were 4,000 at one single event.

---

[50] Author interviews with UNFCCC media representatives. The UNFCCC TV category does not distinguish between reporters, cameramen and technicians, so it is difficult to estimate what percentage are technicians. But if you measure the attendance by organisations, Kyoto had 483 media organisations, whereas Copenhagen had more than double that figure at 1,227.

But it was not just journalists who were present in large numbers. More than 13,000 people were crowded into the Bella Centre at some point. They represented 900 observer organisations, which include UN bodies, intergovernmental organisations, NGOs, trade unions, business groups, other lobby groups, universities, colleges and other research centres.

So Copenhagen was different, and not just because of the numbers. As the Guardian's veteran environment editor John Vidal wrote at the start of the summit, it was 'the only mass media event in history without a proper beginning or an end, which has no genuine celebrities, no fixed agenda, no guaranteed outcome and is unlikely to throw up clear winners or losers'.[51] As we shall see in Chapter 4, it was this uncertainty and drama surrounding the negotiations that dominated the attention of the journalists, and not so much the interest in 'science' symbolised by the presence of hundreds of university academics.

But before that, this chapter summarises the country composition of the journalists present and draws some conclusions about the relative weighting of the different representation of regions, negotiating blocs and rich and poor countries. It also charts the substantial rise in the number of journalists at Copenhagen compared to previous summits at Bali (2007) and Poznan (2008), and the increase in the presence of new media. Finally, it provides an overview of the large numbers of universities represented, and the relative absence of communication officers from these universities compared to those of NGOs and other organisations out in such force at the summit.

Summary of findings

In the interests of brevity, the methodology, the Tables (1 to 10) and the Figures (A1 to A3) providing the background to the examination of the official UNFCCC lists of the people who attended the Copenhagen summits, and the previous ones in Poznan and Bali, can be found in Appendix 2. The following is a summary of the main findings.

Who was at Copenhagen?

- According to the UNFCCC lists, there were 3,877 journalists pre-registered for Copenhagen, and 3,221 who passed through the doors of the Bella Centre.[52] 119 countries were represented, of which 41 were in Europe, 36 in Africa and the Middle East, 23 in Asia-Pacific and 19 in the Americas. Denmark had the most representatives

---

[51] John Vidal, 'A Perfect Storm', *Guardian* (7 Dec. 2009).
[52] The discrepancy between the lower figure of 3,877 we used and the official UNFCCC figure of 3,887 is due to some names appearing twice on UNFCCC lists.

(507), followed by USA (330), Germany (266), France (245) and Japan (239).

- The large number of countries represented (119 countries of the 190-odd involved in the negotiations) disguises the unequal distribution of journalists. Forty of the 119 countries, mostly from the developing world, had only one or two journalists pre-registered, eighty had less than ten. Just ten countries accounted for 66% of the journalists. Sixteen of the top twenty most represented countries were in the developed world.

- As a region, Europe had by far the largest number of journalists present at Copenhagen (2,141 – or 54% of all journalists pre-registered). In contrast there were 25 journalists from the Association of Small Island States (AOSIS), which are far more vulnerable than European countries to the effects of climate change.

Developing countries

- One of the most striking aspects of Copenhagen was the large number of journalists from the G-77 plus China negotiating group: 594 from 68 countries. This figure does not represent a very significant increase from previous COPs in percentage terms (from 12% of all journalists at Bali to 15% at Copenhagen), but it does mean that there was a major increase – measured by absolute numbers – in the representation of poor countries, whose citizens are considered to be most at risk from climate change.[53]

- Twenty-nine of Africa's 54 countries were represented at Copenhagen with 134 journalists, so the average number of journalists per African country represented was less than five. This compares with the European average of 52 and the Asian Pacific one of 26, but it is an increase from the figure for Bali (two per African country).[54]

- The number of journalists from the 49 countries defined by the UN

[53] A good analysis of the 'information gap' can be found in James Fahn's article, 'Rescuing Reporting in the Global South', *Nature Reports Climate Change*, 2 (July 2008): www.nature.com/reports/climatechange. Fahn has slightly different percentage figures to ours for the representation of developing countries at Bali, but this may be explained by a different methodology.

[54] Many of the journalists from African and other developing countries were financed by Western NGOs, Western governments or the UNFCCC's own training programmes (known as Com+). The Climate Change Media Partnership e.g. brought over 40 journalists from 27 countries, many of them from Africa. They wrote more than 500 articles during the two weeks of the summit.

as LDCs (Least Developed Countries) was 102 from 23 of the 49 countries. The figures are swollen in part because of the significant number of journalists from Bangladesh and Nepal. Bangladesh had 38 journalists registered for Copenhagen (more than Russia), whilst Nepal had 17 (more than Greece).

The BRICs (Brazil, Russia, India and China)

- The G-77 figures are heavily influenced by the large numbers of journalists from China (103) and Brazil (100), who figured in the top ten most represented countries in eighth and tenth place respectively.

- The two countries were amongst those with the highest number of journalists travelling with their heads of state who were not registered on the media lists. According to unofficial UNFCCC figures, China, Russia, Brazil, India, Indonesia and the USA provided a high percentage of the 500–700 journalists who accompanied their heads of state.

- Brazil had the largest official delegation of 572 people, but there were not many press representatives among them. Most of its media representatives came from the private sector (15 came from Globo). Denmark had the second largest delegation with 527. China had 333, the USA 274 and the UK 111.

- In effect, the Chinese government paid for the large number of official journalists at Copenhagen in part to counter any anti-Chinese comments coming out of the summit. It had 22 journalists registered to its official delegation.

- In contrast, anecdotal evidence suggests NGOs paid for a significant number of Indian journalists to come to Copenhagen. India's figures increased from 13 journalists in Bali to 43 at Copenhagen, which gave it the third largest G-77 representation.

- Russia increased its representation from just 2 in Bali to 36 in Copenhagen, but it still remained in twenty-first position, below Belgium, Switzerland and Bangladesh.

Presence by negotiating blocs

- The main negotiating blocs at Copenhagen were the 130-odd member countries of the G-77 plus China group, the 27 countries of the EU (of which 26 were represented), the nine countries of the Umbrella Group (which includes the USA, Australia, Canada and Russia) and the three countries of the EIG (Environmental Integrity Group) group (see Appendix 2 and Table 3).

- The EU bloc was by far the most represented (49% of all journalists registered), followed by the Umbrella Group (21%) and the G-77 plus China (15%).

The rise in new media

- The largest media category of the seven at all three summits was television by some margin, although the numbers include technicians as well as journalists.

- Online representation increased nearly five-fold from 54 in Bali to 243 at Copenhagen. Google alone had 33 representatives, whilst the USA had the largest number of online journalists (46), followed by Denmark (32) and the UK (23).

Trends from Bali to Copenhagen

See Figures A1 to A3 in Appendix 2.

- Unsurprisingly, host nations supply a large percentage of the journalists present at COP meetings, although the percentage has varied between Bali and Copenhagen. Indonesia provided 470 at Bali (31% of all journalists there), Poland 325 (39%) at Poznan and Denmark 507 (just 13%) at Copenhagen.

- The geographic location of the summit has a marked impact on the regional splits. So at Bali, the Asia-Pacific region supplied 54% of all journalists, whilst at Poznan and Copenhagen, Europe provided the most (71 and 54% respectively). Europe represented less than a quarter (23%) of the journalists at Bali, whilst Asia-Pacific had 15% at Copenhagen and 10% at Poznan.[55] Japan consistently sends large

---

[55] The figures for Europe would be higher if the international agencies had been assigned regionally.

number of journalists to COP summits.[56]

- In percentage terms and in absolute numbers, Latin America increased its presence significantly, largely due to Brazil. Numbers went up from 32 in Bali to 172 in Copenhagen, whilst percentages went up from 1 (Bali) to 3 (Poznan) to 5 in Copenhagen. The number of Brazilian journalists went up from 14 in Bali to 100 in Copenhagen. Africa and the Middle East's percentage representation remained pretty steady at between 2 and 4%.

- At Bali, there were 175 journalists present from 38 of the 130 member states of the G-77 group, equivalent to 12% of all the journalists there (not including Indonesia). This number dipped at Poznan to 76 from 39, but rose again to 594 from 68 countries by the time of Copenhagen.

- Of these, the number of journalists from LDCs rose five-fold from 23 at Poznan to 102 at Copenhagen, although the percentage figure only increased slightly from 2 to 3%. The number of countries represented also rose from 11 to 23. The average number of journalists from each LDC country increased from two at Poznan to five at Copenhagen. This compares unfavourably with the average for other regions, including Latin America which had an average of ten per country at Copenhagen.

NGOs, universities and communication officers

Large numbers of organisations representing civil society attend COP meetings. At Copenhagen there were more than 12,000 people from 794 such groups.[57] Again, the methodology for our findings can be found in Appendix 2, along with the relevant tables (8 to 10). Our main findings are the following:

- Nearly 1,700 people attended from 88 universities listed under UNFCCC headings. This figures climbs to around 2,000 from nearly 250 universities if all those attending from universities are included. The addition of colleges, academic associations and some research centres raises the figure further to around 2,500.

[56] See Toshiya Kaba, 'Climate Change Journalism: Comparative Study of Japanese Coverage of COP3 and COP14', RISJ fellowship paper, Hilary Term 2009: http://reutersinstitute.politics.ox.ac.uk/fileadmin/documents/Publications/fellows__papers/2008-2009/Kaba_-_Climate_Change_Journalism.pdf.
[57] http://unfccc.int/resource/docs/2009/cop15/eng/inf01p03.pdf, p. 2.

- Of the academics present, 280 of these were listed as professors, the vast majority attached to universities rather than other bodies (listed in Table 9). Some academic conferences draw hundreds of university lecturers and students to attend them. But it is hard to think of a political event other than Copenhagen which has represented such an attraction to the academic world.

- Of the 2,000 academics who were present at Copenhagen registered under a university, it would be surprising if around 500 of them were not senior researchers who had sufficient expertise in some area of the science to be sufficiently authoritative to be quoted by the media. As already mentioned, 280 of the 2,000 were professors, and it would be not too wild a guess to suggest that at least another 10% (i.e. 200) had published peer-reviewed science.

- NGOs like Greenpeace, Oxfam and WWF had large numbers of communication officers working for them at Copenhagen. Greenpeace had 20 (equivalent to 14% of its total delegation), WWF 10 (11%) and Oxfam 6 (8%).[58] Greenpeace had a larger delegation than that of the official UK delegation: 143 compared to 111.

- In contrast, universities had a total of 12 press or communication officers for the 250-odd universities there, and two of these were from a United Nations body, the UN University, which is more like a research centre. So Greenpeace had nearly twice as many, and WWF almost the same number, as the total number working for universities.

- Academic associations do not fare much better than universities. The other two categories of bodies – research centres and UN organisations – have more than universities but still way short of NGOs. It is significant that the IPCC only had one information and communications officer registered. Within the research centres, the three meteorological institutes included (in Denmark, Holland and the UK) all had one or two press or communication officers.[59]

- The UNFCCC list of government delegations reveals far higher

[58] If the ten photographers, one video producer and one editor listed under the Greenpeace entry were included, then Greenpeace would have 32 representatives working on media and communications out of a total delegation of 143 (equivalent to over 20%).
[59] None of these organisations can compete with the numbers of communications experts large companies in the private sector employ. Coca-Cola for example is reported to have employed 38 people from seven different lobbying companies working on its behalf in 2009.

numbers of people working with the media – a total of 288 press or communication workers listed under 85 countries. Denmark had the most listed (46) followed by Sweden and Canada (13 each), France (12), USA (11) and Norway (10).[60]

By way of conclusion, it should be stressed that we do not know how many of the journalists at Copenhagen were environment correspondents with a long track record of reporting climate change, and how many were general news reporters or political correspondents sent to accompany or monitor their heads of state. After all, As John Vidal has written, traditional boundaries between environment journalists and other more generalist reporters have broken down. Political, business and feature writers now turn their hand regularly to the environment. 'To paraphrase Al Gore', he wrote, 'we are all environment journalists now'.[61]

The distinction is important as it may go a long way to explaining what angles the journalists there chose to report on. It is probably safe to assume though that many of the journalists from developing countries were more general reporters, and in many cases, the Western media chose to send both general and environment reporters. For example, the Science Media Centre in Australia knows that many of the Australian journalists sent to Copenhagen were 'political and current affairs reporters rather than science or environment reporters'.[62]

Despite these caveats, the key point is that an unprecedented number of journalists from an unprecedented number of countries, with an unprecedented representation from developing countries, were present at Copenhagen. It was also the case that dozens of academic scientists were amongst the large numbers of representatives from civil society under the same roof as the journalists. It was a unique opportunity for many journalists, particularly those from developing countries, to include some reporting on climate science. So we now turn to an examination of the extent to which the journalists chose to report on the science, and when they did, who they preferred to quote.

---

[60] Papua New Guinea had 13 but most were working for Coalition for Rainforest Nations in which the country is a very active member.
[61] Vidal, 'A Perfect Storm'.
[62] Observation by the SMC Australia in a personal communication with the author, Sept. 2010.

4. The Media's Coverage of Copenhagen

As we saw in Chapter 2, historically there has not been much coverage of climate change in the media in Africa, Latin America and the Middle East, although it is on the rise. But as Figure 2.1 showed, December 2009 witnessed a huge spike. Most of this was due to the Copenhagen summit, although the coverage of the UEA emails also contributed. The 50 newspapers surveyed included 5,700 climate-change-related stories, easily the highest number ever recorded since the monitoring began in January 2004. Even the three papers logged from South Africa and Argentina registered a peak of well over 200 articles in December. The UN's own analysis of more than 6,000 articles in 70 countries covering the Copenhagen summit found that there had been a three-fold increase in coverage of climate change in the world's media compared to the previous summit at Poznan.[63]

The percentage increases from the start of 2009 were highest for South America/Africa (85%), Oceania (79%), Asia/Middle East (68%) and Europe (67%).[64] But even in North America, where the percentage increase was lowest, the rise was 59%. In the USA, the coverage of global warming shot up to more than 10% of all print, online, radio and television news during the first week of the summit. This was the highest amount of coverage registered by the Pew Research Center's Project for Excellence in Journalism since it began tracking percentage coverage of different news topics in January 2007.[65] US television coverage of global warming in the nightly news peaked in 2007 and has been declining since then. But it did see a one-off increase in December

[63] 'United Nations Climate Change Conference: Copenhagen 2009', UN Department of Public Information (DPI) internal report, New York, Sept. 2010, p. 3.
[64] Boykoff, 'Indian Media Representations', p. 19.
[65] Pew Research Center's Project for Excellence in Journalism, 'Economy and Health Lead But Climate Gains Attention', News Coverage Index: 7–13 Dec. 2009: www.journalism.org/index_report/pej_news_coverage_index_december_713_2009.

2009 associated with Copenhagen.[66] As we saw in Chapter 2, this spike in the USA came after a general downward trend in environmental coverage, including climate, from 2007 and 2008 to just 1.5% of all news coverage. The private life of golfer Tiger Woods, the 'balloon boy' who turned out to be a hoax and the White House party crashers all received more coverage in 2009 – until Copenhagen.

The volume of coverage in the USA was hardly surprising given the 330 American journalists who had registered for the summit. But as shown in the previous chapter, it was not just the American media who were there in force. Of the 4,000 journalists there, 266 journalists were pre-registered from Germany – the third largest country representation – prompting saturation coverage: 'every newspaper, every news magazine, every online outlet covered the conference with special sections, special reports, and special attention generally (and not only in the science sections).'[67] But as we have seen, the media in developing countries were also well-represented. For the first time, nearly 600 journalists travelled to Copenhagen from developing countries, more than three times than the number in Bali. More than 40 journalists were present from India, and 'for the first time climate change became mainstream news and was telecast in prime time news and front page reports.'[68]

But in what sense did climate change become mainstream news in a way that had seldom been seen before in the media of most countries? Was it only about the negotiations or did climate science get a look in? After all, Copenhagen represented an excellent opportunity for many journalists to include in their reporting aspects of climate science and to explain the background to the science to an audience who may not have been fully versed in all its complexity, variety and uncertainties.

The focus of this chapter then is on how much the science of climate change was included in the media in 12 different countries; when the science was discussed, who got quoted on the science (politicians, NGOs, scientists or sceptics); and whose reactions were most sought to the Copenhagen Accord signed at the end of the summit by Brazil, USA, South Africa, India and China?

Methodology of the study

The 12 countries selected for the content analysis were Australia, Brazil, China, Egypt, India, Italy, Mexico, Nigeria, Russia, UK, USA and Vietnam. They were chosen to ensure a good representation of:

---

[66] Quoted in Revkin, 'The Greatest Story Rarely Told'.
[67] Knight Science Journalism Tracker, 'German Language Media: Why Copenhagen Failed': http://ksjtracker. mit.edu/2009/12/29/german-lang-media-why-copenhagen-failed/.
[68] Observation from Kushal Pal Singh Yadav, Centre for Science and Environment, Delhi.

- the five different geographical regions (Africa-Middle East, Asia-Pacific, Europe, the USA and Latin America) used in the categorisation of media representatives in Chapter 3;

- major players in the negotiations (Australia, Brazil, China, India, USA, EU);

- the four BRIC countries (Brazil, Russia, India and China);

- English-language (Australia, Nigeria, India, UK and the USA) and non-English-language publications (Brazil, China, Egypt, India, Italy, Mexico, Russia and Vietnam);

- countries particularly vulnerable to climate change impacts (Brazil, Vietnam, Egypt, China);

- countries with different media landscapes and political systems.[69]

We recognise that the culture of journalism and the media landscape in which it operates vary enormously from country to country. Newspapers from these different media systems are very difficult to compare directly, and it would have been nigh on impossible to find equivalent print media to compare in all 12 countries.

However, as a norm, in each country we chose two daily newspapers with an online presence: the first was usually a broadsheet newspaper aimed mainly at AB socio-economic groups and the second was a 'tabloid' newspaper, not defined by its size or format but by its target audience (as being more 'populist' in its subject matter and aimed at lower socio-economic groups).

A particular obstacle was that many countries do not share the tabloid culture of the UK or have an obvious equivalent newspaper to the *Daily Mail* or *Sun*. This was true for example of Egypt, which does not have a daily tabloid newspaper. In this instance the second paper chosen was *al-Masri al-Youm*, which is privately owned and a major challenger to the dominant state-owned print media. In the case of India, two broadsheet newspapers were reviewed of which one was in English and the other in Hindi, again because there is not a strong tabloid culture. Although *Dainik Baskar* probably has a higher socio-economic target group than most British tabloids, relative to the *Times of India*, its readership includes lower income groups.

---

[69] We did not seek a balance of left-leaning and right-leaning newspapers, although in fact there was a good representation of the political spectrum.

In China, the *People's Daily* was chosen to represent the broadsheet press and the *Beijing Evening News* the tabloid press. The former is the mouthpiece of the Chinese Communist Party, whereas the latter is aimed at a more general audience whose taste tends to be more focused on 'very quotidian or sensationalist topics such as shopping, entertainment, crime and disasters, as well as the government-dominated headlines'.[70]

In the case of Vietnam, two online portals were chosen rather than newspapers with an online presence. The first (VietnamNet) is a Hanoi-based online news portal, whereas Zing is a Ho Chi Minh-based entertainment portal which includes some news. Vietnamese newspapers are not included in Factiva or Lexis-Nexis search facilities, so online portals were chosen in part because they have their own search engines. But it is also worth pointing out that internet penetration in Vietnam has grown enormously from virtually nothing in 1997 to over 22 million users in 2009 (equivalent to more than a quarter of the population).[71]

The full list of papers or online sites included is:[72]

> Australia (*Sydney Morning Herald, Daily Telegraph*)
> Brazil (*Folha de Sao Paulo, Super Noticia*)
> China (*People's Daily, Beijing Evening News*)
> Egypt (*al-Akhbar, al-Masri al-Youm*)
> India (*Times of India, Dainik Baskar*)
> Italy (*Corriere della Sera, Il Giorno*)
> Mexico (*Reforma, Uno Más Uno*)
> Nigeria (*Guardian, Sun*)
> Russia (*Kommersant, Komsomolskaya Pravda*)
> United Kingdom (*Guardian, Daily Mail*)
> USA (*New York Times, New York Post*)
> Vietnam (VietnamNet, Zing)

Where possible, the researchers accessed the online versions of the newspapers using the Factiva or Lexis-Nexis search facilities (Italy, UK, USA and *Reforma* in Mexico). In other cases, the papers' own search engines were used (Brazil, India, *Uno Más Uno* in Mexico, Nigeria, Russia and Vietnam). In Australia, it was ProQuest. The key words 'Copenhagen' and 'climate change', or their equivalent in the local language, were entered for the search.

In the case of China, the hardcopy version of the two newspapers was

---

[70] Rebecca Nadin, personal communication with the author.
[71] Giang Nguyen, 'When Lack of Impartiality Makes an Impact: A Comparative Study of VietCatholic and the BBC', RISJ fellows paper, June 2010, p. 4.
[72] Short profiles of these papers or online sites can be found in Appendix 3.

analysed, as the online version would have given only a small sample. In addition, the *People's Daily* and *People's Daily Online* are two separate publications. Although they both belong to People's Daily Group, they have separate management and staffing. In the case of Egypt, hard copies were also used as *al-Akhbar* does not have a functioning search facility.

Six 24-hour blocks were monitored, three at the start of the summit (Monday 8 December to Wednesday 10 December) and three at the end of the summit (Thursday 18 December to Saturday 20 December).[73] In some cases, a paper's sister weekend or Sunday publication was included in the last day of monitoring (*Sunday Telegraph* and *Sunday Herald* in Australia, and the *Observer* and the *Mail on Sunday* in the UK for example).

The articles were selected on the basis of reports from or about the Copenhagen summit. We included background specials and articles not by-lined from Copenhagen but mentioning Copenhagen in a substantive way. Comment pieces, editorials, op eds and letters were not included, nor were authored pieces written by scientists about some aspect of the science. We did not distinguish between reports published based on agency reports (AFP, AP or Reuters, for example) and those based on reports from the papers' own correspondents at Copenhagen. Nor did we assess or measure the length of each article, where it appeared in the newspaper or on the page, the headlines or photos used, nor how the science of climate change was framed (for example, an alarmist 'doom and gloom' versus a positive 'solutions-oriented' tone, or the dominance of 'the West is to blame for the impacts' narrative).

We were strict about the application of the publishing time of the articles. This led to some background articles or reports on the science of climate change being omitted. For example, background pieces strongly linked to Copenhagen and published before or after the summit were not included, but those published on the opening Monday, Tuesday and Wednesday were included (from the UK *Guardian*, *Kommersant* and Australia's *Daily Telegraph* for example). The results from Vietnam, Nigeria and Egypt would have been different if we had included different dates.[74]

The text of the research questionnaire filled in for each country can be found in Appendix 4.

The first measurement we made was of how many articles about the

[73] The periods monitored were from 0000 to 2359 GMT each day, so the whole period ran from 0000 GMT Monday 8 Dec. to 2359 GMT Wednesday 10 Dec., and from 0000 GMT Thursday 18 Dec. to 2359 Saturday 20 Dec. 2010.

[74] VietnamNet e.g. published dozens of articles on its site about the science in the run-up to the summit, which reflected the international news and the conferences held in Vietnam and attended by Vietnamese scientists about the country's vulnerability to climate change impacts. In Nigeria, the *Guardian* published an in-depth study in its hard copy version of the paper in the Homes and Property section entitled 'The Nigeria Climate Report', but because it did not appear in the online version, it was not included in the review. *Al-Masri al-Youm* published an article on 21 Dec. which included discussion of the latest science of climate change and quoted a number of scientists.

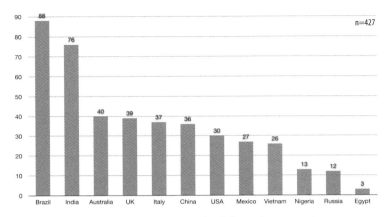

Figure 4.1. Number of articles published at start and end of Copenhagen summit

Copenhagen summit were published on each day of the six days monitored. Appendix 5 shows all the results broken down by country and paper/online site. Figure 4.1 shows the country variations for the total amount of articles published over the six days. Of the 427 articles that were published, Brazil had the most with 88, Egypt the least with 3. The three individual papers with the most coverage were *Folha de Sao Paulo* (86), *Times of India* (52) and the (UK) *Guardian* (34). All but three of the broadsheet newspapers (Nigeria, Russia and Egypt) published 19 or more articles.

Figure 4.2 shows the total amount of articles published in broadsheet papers compared to 'tabloids'. The totals include all the papers classified as 'tabloid'. In general, there was considerably less coverage in the tabloid than in the

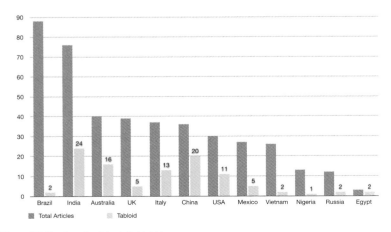

Figure 4.2. Number of articles in 'tabloids'

broadsheet press. Of the 427 articles surveyed, under a quarter (103) were to be found in the 'tabloids'.

The second principal measurement was to evaluate how many of the articles were about the 'science of climate change'. This was defined as discussion of temperature rises, the link to GHG emissions, IPCC reports, other reports on the science, sea-level rises, ice melt in its various forms, the science of carbon capture and storage or other 'geo-engineering' solutions, but not REDD (reducing emissions from deforestation and forest degradation) or mitigation or adaptation schemes where the focus was not clearly the science.[75] Discussion of 'Climategate' was also included as it was considered to be about the science of climate change to a significant extent.

For each of the articles included, an assessment was made of how much of the science of climate change was mentioned or discussed. This was usually carried out by counting the number of paragraphs about the science contained in the article, and dividing them by the total number of paragraphs in the article. If for example there were 20 articles published for the period in question, the 20 articles were divided into the three categories of 0–10, 10–50 and 51–100%.

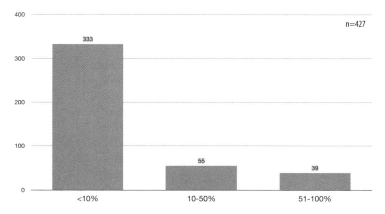

Figure 4.3. Number of articles by percentage discussing science

Figure 4.3 shows the percentage breakdown for each of the three categories. Of the articles 78% (equivalent to 333 articles) had less than 10% dedicated to the science, 13% (55) had between 10 and 50%, and 9% (39) had more than 50%.

[75] An impressionistic appraisal would be that there were few articles published about REDD, or on the details of mitigation and adaptation schemes. However, there was considerable coverage of the negotiations on the amount of money on offer from developed to developing countries for such schemes.

The next measurements (questions 5 and 6 of the questionnaire) were of which organisations or individuals were quoted just about the science of climate change.[76] We did not include the frequent comments from these organisations or individuals about other topics, for example, how the negotiations were proceeding. These were broken down into the IPCC/UNFCCC, other international bodies (such as UNEP, the WMO, the Red Cross, etc.), national organisations like governments and state bodies such as the EPA in the USA or Met Office in the UK, NGOs (like Greenpeace, Oxfam, etc.), scientists usually from universities and research institutes (with and without the generic category of 'scientists'), sceptics and other (which included the business sector).

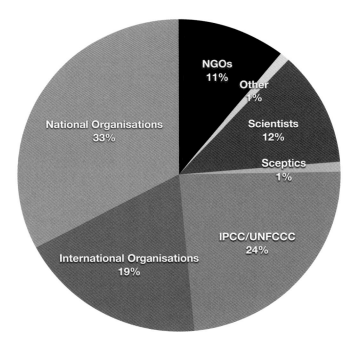

Figure 4.4. Who was quoted on the science?

Figure 4.4 shows the breakdown by category expressed as a percentage. Of the 233 times the different bodies or individuals were quoted, national organisations such as the UK Met Office and the Environment Protection

---

[76] Graphics, maps or other illustrations quoting the organisations as the source were included. 'Quoted' was taken to include direct and indirect speech.

Agency in the US were quoted the most (77 times), followed by the IPCC/ UNFCCC (55 times), other international bodies like the WMO (44 times), scientists from universities and research centres (28 times),[77] NGOs (25 times), sceptics (twice) and other (twice). The figure combines the results from questions 5 and 6 of the questionnaire.

The figure does not include the 22 times 'scientists' were quoted generically in the articles reviewed. If they had been, then their percentage would have gone up to 21%.

The category of 'sceptics' was defined broadly to include those who believe that climate change is a natural fluctuation and not caused principally by man-made greenhouse gases, those who believe that the current and future impacts have been severely exaggerated, and/or those who believe that immediate action is not necessary. In all 427 articles, named sceptics were

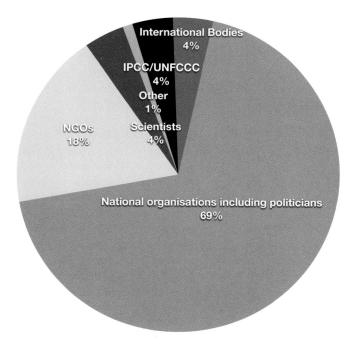

Figure 4.5. Who was quoted at the end of the summit?

[77] It was a limitation of the text of the research questionnaire that question 6 allowed for individual scientists from government bodies and NGOs as well as universities and research centres to be included. The actual total of scientists taken from the relevant rows of the figure in Appendix 5 is 34. However, if we disaggregate the results, it transpires that, of the 34 scientists who are quoted, 27 are from universities or research centres, 6 from government bodies and one is a historian/academic (whom we counted as being from a university). Hence we arrived at the total of 28 for universities/research centres and 77 for national organisations.

only quoted twice on the science, although the generic term 'sceptics' was used four times. This latter figure has not been included to be consistent with the non-inclusion in the figure of the generic category of 'scientists'.

The final measurement was of who got quoted at the end of the summit on their reaction to the Copenhagen Accord signed by Brazil, USA, South Africa, India and China. The categories used were the same as those used in questions 5 and 6, so politicians, who were widely quoted, were included in the category of national organisations and governments. Figure 4.5 shows the percentage breakdown for each category. Of the 244 individuals who were quoted, 167 were representatives of governments or national organisations, 44 were from NGOs, 10 were scientists, 10 were from international bodies, 9 were from the IPCC/UNFCCC, and 4 were other (of which one was a sceptic). It is worth pointing out that of the 10 scientists quoted, six were to be found in the *Observer* (20 December). The *Observer* also quoted the largest number of NGOs (15) for their reactions, followed by *Folha de Sao Paulo* (6). Both the UK and Brazil have a very active NGO presence lobbying on climate change issues.

Discussion of the findings

Country variations

It should be stated at the outset that a different selection of newspapers to monitor may of course have resulted in significantly different results. But the variation we monitored between countries in the amount of coverage is not out of line with other studies. In our study, Brazil had the most, followed by India, Australia and the UK. The much more comprehensive study by the UN also found that Brazil had the highest volume of coverage of the summit, followed by the UK and Northern Ireland, the United States, India and Iran.[78]

As we saw in Chapter 2, Brazil often emerges as a country whose media pay a lot of attention to the issue of climate change. There are a multitude of reasons for this: many of Brazil's main newspapers and magazines, including ones specialising on the economy, have their own science or environment correspondents. TV Globo, which by repute is the largest private media company in the world and dominates the domestic media landscape, frequently covers the issue.[79]

The possibility that the internet offers for increasing the volume of articles published is another factor why Brazil comes out top. *Folha de Sao Paulo* is typical of Brazilian websites in taking the view that 'more is better'. Our

[78] UN DPI internal report, p. 9.
[79] Its main evening news broadcast has an estimated audience of 30 million viewers, compared to *Folha de Sao Paulo*'s readership of about 300,000.

research showed that many of the articles published on the site were based on agency material (particularly AP and EFE) as well as from their own correspondents. It also showed that more than 70% of the articles monitored from *Folha de Sao Paulo* only appeared on the website and not in the hardcopy of the paper. A cursory examination suggests it was on the website that science and scientists had more of an opportunity to be heard, whereas the print version concentrated on the Copenhagen negotiations and gave much less of the science.[80]

The greater space for coverage supplied by the net is a key factor too in explaining the position of the next two papers by volume of coverage (the UK *Guardian* and the *Times of India*). The *Guardian* prides itself on presenting very comprehensive coverage of climate change on guardian.co.uk, and has a separate subsection under that title (www.guardian.co.uk/environment/climate-change). The *Times of India* website published a large number of articles which used agency sources like PTI, AFP, and Reuters as well as its own correspondents.

VietnamNet also relied heavily on international news agencies and non-Vietnamese sources of information. Indeed, the amount of coverage in the Vietnam media has been growing steadily from a low base in 2006,[81] so it should come as no surprise that there was a reasonable quantity of coverage in the two online portals surveyed. Neither VietnamNet nor Zing appears to have had a correspondent at Copenhagen and yet the number of articles, at least in VietnamNet, was relatively high for a developing country. An analysis of two Vietnamese papers carried out by a RISJ fellow in March 2009 of media interest in the December 2008 Poznan summit also suggested a significant amount of coverage (four long articles in *Tuoi Tre* and several in *Nhan Dan*). Amongst the factors cited for explaining the increase were the growing amount of concern from government officials about the impacts of climate change on Vietnam, and the fact that the prime minister is from the Mekong Delta, one of the areas most vulnerable in the world to sea-level rises. Another factor is the increase in training in recent years offered by Internews' Earth Journalism Network to journalists in Vietnam.[82]

It should also come as no surprise that two of the three countries with the least coverage should be in Africa. As discussed in Chapter 2, the African media usually pay less attention to climate change than the media in other countries. In a survey of two print media in 13 countries carried out by RISJ journalist fellows and presented at a RISJ/ECI seminar held in Oxford on 26

---

[80] Observations by the Brazilian researcher, Leticia Sorg.

[81] Shanahan, , 'Time to Adapt?', p. 152.

[82] See Lloyd and Russell, 'Better Communication Begets Trust', *The Observatory: Columbia Journalism Review* (23 Feb. 2010). EJN's executive director, James Fahn, suggests there has been a steady rise in coverage with locally sourced material since 2006.

February 2010, another African country, Ethiopia, emerged as third from last (above only Russia and Egypt) with only seven articles.[83]

There is some evidence to suggest that the South African media may have been an exception. In results presented at the ECI/RISJ seminar, the *Mail and Guardian* published 21 articles about Copenhagen on 7/8 and 18/19 December, whilst *Business Day* published 5 articles. Both newspapers had two correspondents at Copenhagen registered for the event. It appears that the two newspapers chosen for the content analysis for this study from Nigeria (the *Guardian* and the *Sun*) did not have correspondents there, but the two newspapers chosen for Egypt did. The results may of course have been significantly different if print media with correspondents present had always been selected. [84]

Russian coverage of climate change in general is very low compared to other countries, perhaps reflecting the low level of concern amongst the Russian political elite and the elite dominance of the news agenda in the Russian media. A study carried out by the MediaClimate Project in 2010 of 2,500 articles covering Copenhagen in two print media in 18 countries concluded that 'Russian coverage remains at an astonishingly low level'.[85] The study included, as ours did, the leading business newspaper, *Kommersant*. An analysis by a RISJ fellow of the coverage of the Poznan summit in 2008 showed that the same newspaper mentioned the summit in its calendar of events, but there was no follow-up. *Moskovskyi Komsomolets*, a tabloid, published one short news story where Poznan was mentioned. However, the story was not about the meeting itself but the fact that a French ambassador who was at Poznan had told a joke about George W. Bush.

It is worth returning briefly to the possible relationship between the amount of coverage in the media and public awareness or concern. Our survey once again confirmed the low amount of coverage in Russia and the Middle East compared to other nations. It may be no coincidence that people in Russia and Middle Eastern countries often figure as some of the least concerned about climate change. For example, the BBC/Globescan 2009 poll mentioned in the notes of Chapter 2 put Russia in penultimate position of the 23 countries, with 46% seeing climate change as a very serious problem. One of the most extensive surveys of attitudes towards climate change carried out by Nielsen in 2007 was based on interviews with 25,000 internet users in 47 countries. In

[83] The order by volume of coverage in the thirteen countries monitored was India, Japan, UK, Brazil, Italy Vietnam, Nigeria, Finland, Samoa, Singapore, Ethiopia, Russia and Egypt. The number of articles surveyed was 268. The survey applied similar criteria to the content analysis in this study but involved fewer dates (7, 8, 18 and 19 Dec.).

[84] However, the presence of correspondents does not necessarily result in high coverage. *Al-Akhbar* had two correspondents registered, but at least in the days surveyed the coverage was minimal.

[85] Eide et al., 'Domesticating a Global Moment'. The MediaClimate project is coordinated by the Universities of Oslo and Tampere. Its findings at the time of writing are preliminary.

Box 4.1: China: A Case Study

The coverage

During the period of analysis, the *Beijing Evening News* and the *People's Daily* ran comparable amounts of coverage. The main difference was in the style and substance. Perhaps surprisingly for a 'tabloid' media, the quality of the reporting in *Beijing Evening News* was significantly higher than that featured in the *People's Daily*. Although not overtly analytical, the editorial stance taken attempted to inform and unpick the issues and explain the political process for the reader. Issues covered included examination of the leading players, political and economic interests, climate financing and an explanation of China's contribution to meeting emission targets.

In the *People's Daily*, there was limited coverage of senior Chinese leaders meeting with Western diplomats or political elites. The majority of coverage at the start of the conference concentrated on positioning China as a developing nation with a strong focus on the concept of 'common but differentiated responsibility'. Coverage was dedicated to China's engagement with the leaders of countries that were more supportive or aligned to China's stance such as the BRIC nations or developing countries. Not surprisingly, in the lead-up to and during the conference, the coverage clearly reflected China's own negotiating position. In the first instance, when discussing targets and financial commitments, media coverage positioned China as a developing nation and as a champion of the G-77 agenda. However, once the outcome of the negotiations was clear, coverage switched to include Chinese leaders meeting with Indian, UK and German counterparts, thus positioning it as a responsible world power. This clearly demonstrates the dichotomy for China's leaders: developing/emerging nation or world superpower.

Although important, the coverage of the conference and the science did not dominate. The end of the conference happened to coincide with the tenth anniversary of the return of Macau to China (20 December), and subsequently both newspapers used a significant amount of column inches to cover the anniversary. *Beijing Evening News* coverage of the conference was also competing against domestic and social news such as employment rates, medical care, food prices, the stock market, housing and corruption cases. As expected, the *People's Daily* continued to run traditional coverage of official visits to other countries by President Hu Jintao and Premier Wen Jiabao. It is interesting to note, however, that both papers used this opportunity to increase coverage of potentially controversial issues such as environmental protection, desertification and water management.

Who got quoted?

In both the *Beijing Evening News* and the *People's Daily* the number of Chinese scientists quoted was limited, with more column inches given to overseas experts. In addition, there was no reference to Chinese scientific reports; again overseas reports were quoted. There are several reasons for this. First, there is not a tradition of Chinese scientists engaging in public science communication activities. When commentary was given by Chinese scientists regarding COP-15, it was about the politics rather than the science. In China, as in other countries, many science topics, especially climate change, are related to national policy such as energy security.

If you include the online edition of the *People's Daily*, a total of nine named scientists/academics were listed. In general when non-Chinese scientists/academics were quoted it was to emphasise the plight of developing countries and impact of climate change on them. For example, four of the named non-Chinese nationals were used to highlight the impacts of climate change on Bangkok and Brazil.

Climate change in general is not particularly sensitive as a topic, unlike other issues such as human rights, environmental pollution or Tibet. However, given the high level of political engagement in the conference, it is no surprise that scientists and academics would have exercised a degree of self-censorship. The issue is not as simple as 'censorship', self- or state-imposed. Politics, societal concerns and power relations are much more deeply embedded in the Chinese consciousness than science. This is the legacy of centuries of religious, philosophical and even literary thought. Although in ancient times China dominated the world in scientific discovery, in more modern times Chinese scientific achievement has fallen behind. China's government realises this and thus is pushing hard for China to become a scientifically informed nation, but it is a challenge given that even scientists are often embroiled in politics. In addition, journalists are more inclined to interview government officials (when possible) rather than academics. This is because academics will often give different views to accepted government policy and, therefore, details of the interview cannot be reported.

Another major challenge facing science journalists is their lack of knowledge of scientific topics, which causes difficulties in their communication with the scientists. This is linked to the entry paths to journalism. Most practising journalists come from journalism degree courses or arts and letters backgrounds. Science and technology graduates are unlikely to go into journalism since the demand for their skills and opportunities for jobs is so vast in China's industrial sector. Consequently, the general level of technical awareness of science journalists in China is rather low.

Analysis by Dr Rebecca Nadin, Director Climate Change Programme, British Council, Beijing.

the survey, Russia and Egypt were second and third last respectively as rating global warming a major concern.[86]

Broadsheets versus tabloids

The large variation between the numbers of articles published in broadsheets compared to 'tabloids' is heavily influenced by the weight of the number of articles printed on the *Folha de Sao Paulo* website (86) compared to *Super Noticia* (2). Brazil does not have a strong tabloid culture, and those that do exist tend to focus on local issues. Coverage of international issues is seen as somewhat elitist and could explain why the paper gave such little importance to the conference.[87] This could explain part of the disparity in other countries too. Another factor is the reduced space available in tabloids compared to broadsheets. But the potential of space available on the website could mitigate this difference.

There were only two countries where there was more coverage in the 'tabloids'. China's *Beijing Evening News* had slightly more articles, but the main difference was more in style and substance than quantity (see Box 4.1). In the case of Egypt the sample was too small to be significant.

The study of Copenhagen by the MediaClimate project also found that, with the usual caveats about the usage of the words 'elite' and 'popular' newspapers,

---

[86] Nielsen Global Online survey, 4 June 2007. Of the 47 countries, Australia came 3rd, Brazil 7th, India 16th, Mexico 17th, Italy 20th, the UK 27th, South Africa 32nd, USA 33rd, China 37th and Vietnam 38th. Nigeria was not included.
[87] Observations by the Brazil researcher, Leticia Sorg. Despite the lack of coverage, *Super Noticia* did publish two letters from readers about Copenhagen on 19 and 20 Dec.

the coverage in the latter was low compared to the newspapers more oriented to the elite political agendas. The researchers concluded that:

> This offers further support to the idea that a transnational political process of climate in journalism is dealt with mostly within the conditions and frames set by the national political fields and the ways in which 'climate change' as a problem is placed to the public agenda is run importantly by national political power elites.[88]

In general, the lower levels of coverage in the 'tabloids' may be a cause of concern for those Western governments and NGOs who want to see climate change rise as an issue of major concern for the public in general. There is strong evidence to suggest that it is not as popular or popularised an issue as these groups would want.[89]

The amount of articles dedicated to the science

As Figure 4.3 shows, just 39 of the 427 articles monitored (9%) from or about Copenhagen had more than half the article dedicated to the science. A more detailed discussion of why this might be so is set out in Chapter 5. But it is worth pointing out that the 9% figure would have been reduced further if we had decided to exclude background articles not written from Copenhagen but with strong reference to Copenhagen. 'Climategate' was covered by a number of papers at the start of the conference, either as a whole article dedicated to the topic or as a number of paragraphs included in an article.[90] This too had the effect of slightly increasing the percentage of articles in the over 50% category.

Moreover, the inclusion of articles published on 9 December in the review also swelled the percentage as it was the day many papers covered the joint statement by the WMO and the UK Met Office that the 2000s was the warmest decade ever recorded.

Of the 39 articles with more than 50% covering the science, 22 (or 56%) were to be found in the four Western countries (Australia, Italy, the UK and the USA) included in the study.

---

[88] Eide et al., 'Domesticating a Global Moment', p. 9.
[89] A similar conclusion is drawn from the CERES study of Ghana, China and Norway.
[90] Amongst those papers wholly or partially covering Climategate on 7 or 8 Dec. were the *New York Times*, *New York Post*, *Folha de Sao Paulo*, the *Sydney Morning Herald*, *Corriere della Sera*, and the *Guardian* in Nigeria and the UK. It was not mentioned directly in the Chinese media monitored. The US TV channels CNN, Fox News and ABC, all dedicated special reports to the issue.

Who got quoted?

It is interesting to note that in the articles reviewed scientists from universities and research institutes were not heavily quoted on the science of climate change. It may not be surprising that the first three categories quoted were organisations that regularly put out reports on the science. Indeed, as already mentioned, the EPA, the UK Met Office and the WMO all published reports which coincided with the dates in question. In addition, many scientists work for, or are associated with, these organisations. However, given the hundreds of scientists from universities and research centres present at the Bella Centre, it is surprising that these scientists represented only 12% of those quoted on the science. They were quoted on only three more occasions than NGOs.

University scientists were quoted the most in the Australian and Indian press (6 times), followed by Brazil, China and the USA all with 4. NGOs were quoted by far the most in the Indian (10) and the UK press (8), and of these, the majority were to be found in the *Times of India* (6) and the *Guardian* (8). The fact that these two papers represented more than half the times the NGOs were quoted does prompt some caution in ascribing too much weight to a comparison between scientists and NGOs. The *Guardian* generally quotes NGOs widely, so a different choice of UK newspaper could have significantly altered the relative weighting.

At first sight it is surprising that the IPCC/UNFCCC was quoted the second most often (23%, or 55 times) on the science given that the IPCC employs one salaried staff member to handle all the media operations – a remarkably under-resourced communication operation for what is the most important international scientific body working on climate science and a situation that has compounded some of its recent problems (see Box 6.2). However, an unpicking of the statistics would suggest that many of the times when the IPCC/UNFCCC were quoted, it tended to be the IPCC 2007 reports or Yvo de Boer, the UNFCCC's executive secretary. Dr Pachauri, the IPCC chairman, was often in the media for his response to 'Climategate', but there were few if any quotes from IPCC representatives on the science of climate change.

China is particularly interesting for several reasons. First, in the two Chinese media surveyed more column inches were given to overseas experts than Chinese scientists. In addition, there were no references to Chinese scientific reports, but overseas reports were quoted (see Box 4.1). Partly, as Rebecca Nadin writes, this was due to there not being 'a tradition of Chinese scientists engaging in public science communication. When commentary was given by Chinese scientists at Copenhagen, it was about the politics, rather than the science.'

Secondly, in our study, scientists were quoted four times (on the science) in the Chinese media compared to NGOs being quoted once. Several other studies suggest that China is an exception to the general pattern that NGOs are quoted more than scientists. For example, the CERES study, though it was covering general reporting of climate change and not UN summits, concluded that in China the science and academic community were the source for 11% of the stories surveyed compared to just 3% for NGOs.[91] Likewise a study of 91 stories in the Chinese media between 1998 and 2008 found that 76% of them used the 'political establishment' as the source on climate change, 31% scientists or research bodies and just 3% environmental groups.[92]

Sceptics

It is also of considerable note that only two individual sceptics were quoted on the science, and they were to be found in the Western press. The two were Professor Richard Lindzen from the MIT (quoted in Italy's *Corriere della Sera*), and the Canadian blogger-sceptic Stephen McIntyre (quoted in the *New York Times*).[93] A third – Dr Benny Peiser – was quoted in the *Observer* for his reaction to the Accord. Dr Peiser is director of the Global Warming Policy Foundation, an influential sceptical think-tank in the UK.

'Sceptics' were quoted generically four times in the Brazilian, Nigerian and Indian press, but without being named. The media in developing countries did not quote individual sceptics at all, except for one taxi driver in the *Times of India*. This was largely due to the fact that the coverage of 'Climategate', where most sceptics would be expected to be quoted, was concentrated mainly in developed countries, primarily the UK and the US. Only 20% of the coverage on 'Climategate' originated in developing countries.[94]

But it does also seem to be in line with a general trend of the media in developing countries quoting sceptics much less than the media in the Western press. For example, in China, studies have shown that the media seem to be less inclined than their Western counterparts to include the opposite opinion of everything that they are reporting on about climate change.[95] Likewise, the research carried out in 2009 by the RISJ journalist fellow on Chinese media coverage of climate change found that:

> *The debate between climate scientists ... and climate sceptics denying its severity or questioning the source in human*

[91] Coulter and Midttun (eds), 'Escaping Climate Change', p. 57.
[92] Yan Wu, 'The Good, the Bad, and the Ugly', in Boyce and Lewis (eds), *Climate Change and the Media*, pp. 162–3.
[93] Four sceptics were used in Australia's *Daily Telegraph*, but as they were the authors of the pieces, they were excluded from the sample as being more like opinion pieces. The four were Ian Plimer, Bob Carter, David Evans and Walter Starck.
[94] UN DPI internal report, p. 26.
[95] Coulter and Midttun (eds), 'Escaping Climate Change', p. 51.

> *activity, which has featured so prominently in western
> debates over climate change, has never been a significant axis
> in the public discussion of climate change in China.*[96]

This is unsurprising given the role the Chinese media generally play in closely following the official government line on any issue, but it is of interest that the CERES study found that the Norwegian press – an example of the Western media again – was the only one of the three it included to devote any significant space to contrarian views on climate change. By contrast, the Ghanaian media had just one mention.[97] Neither Vietnam nor Mexico had any mention of sceptics, either generically or individually. In the Vietnam online media surveyed, science was often quoted as an essential part of the coverage, but sceptical arguments were nowhere to be found.[98]

Again in contrast to the Western media, sceptics are rarely heard in India. A study of 147 articles published in the Indian press between January 2002 and June 2007 showed that no space was given to sceptics, and 98% of articles attributed climate change to anthropogenic causes.[99] In Peru, 'the media almost universally accepted anthropogenic climate change as reality', whilst in the African media there is a 'near total absence of climate change contrarians'.[100]

It is to be borne in mind that in some of the Western newspapers we reviewed, the voices of sceptics were more likely to be found in op eds and editorial pieces. This was the case, for example, in the *New York Times* and the *New York Post*. It is also true in general of Brazilian newspapers. However, there were a number of sceptics present at the Bella Centre in Copenhagen, and at the alternative conference organised on 8 December by the Danish group of sceptics called Climate Sense. Lord Monckton and Professor Ian Plimer were amongst those at the conference.[101] In general, though, it does seem that they were largely ignored.[102]

Finally, it is of interest that, in the articles reviewed, very few representatives of the business sector were quoted on anything, including the science of climate change. This is perhaps surprising given that the sector was present in large numbers at the Summit and is a hugely influential lobby group. Different results

---

[96] Larson, 'Coverage of Climate Change in the Chinese Media'.
[97] Coulter and Midttun (eds), 'Escaping Climate Change', p. 54.
[98] Comment from Vietnam researcher, Giang Nguyen.
[99] Billett, 'Dividing Climate Change'.
[100] Waite, 'Apathy in the Andes', p. 23; Evelyn Tagbo, 'Media Coverage of Climate Change in Africa', p. 33.
[101] See Louise Gray, 'Copenhagen Climate Summit: Global Warming "Caused by Sun's Radiation"': www.telegraph.co.uk/earth/copenhagen-climate-change-confe/6762640/Copenhagen-climate-summit-global-warming-caused-by-suns-radiation.html (accessed July 2010).
[102] Curtis Brainard and Cristine Russell, 'Copenhagen Watch: Disarray in Denmark?', *The Observatory: Columbia Journalism Review* (9 December 2009): www.cjr.org/the_observatory/copenhagen_watch_disarray_in_d.php.

may have been achieved if more business-oriented papers had been included.[103]

Reactions to the Accord

It is entirely to be expected that national organisations, and in this case mainly governments, should be easily the most quoted sector for their reaction to the Copenhagen Accord. After all, 120 heads of state were present, and it was a political accord hammered out by governments. Nor should it be surprising that the NGO sector should be the second most quoted given their ubiquitous media operations and their presence in significant numbers on the last two days, despite the restrictions on numbers at the Bella Centre.

Only 300 representatives from the NGO sector, which included scientists from universities, were allowed into the Centre on the Thursday and Friday (18 and 19 December). This compares to the several thousand present during the first week of the summit. Possibly as few as 40 scientists were among the 300. Only ten scientists were quoted for their reactions to the Accord. It is difficult to assess from the articles reviewed whether they were in Copenhagen when they were being quoted, but it is a fair bet that many of them were probably not.

Although TV coverage of the end of the summit was not included in this review, a study of two news bulletins on BBC World News and Al Jazeera English at 0500 GMT on 19 December showed that government officials and NGOs were widely quoted, but no scientists. The two news channels ran clips from the same three NGOs: Friends of the Earth, WWF and Greenpeace.[104]

Conclusions

In summary the six main conclusions of the content analysis are the following:

1. The surveys showed that there were strong country variations in the amount of coverage of the Copenhagen summit. However, the main distinction was not between the media in developed and developing countries. Two of the large developing countries – Brazil and India – had the most. Nigeria, Russia and Egypt had the least. Seven of the 12 countries surveyed fell within the 20–40 range for the number of articles; of these seven, four are from developed countries (Australia, UK, Italy and the USA) and three are from developing countries (China, Mexico and Vietnam).

---

[103] Fiona Harvey, the *FT*'s environment correspondent, said that, in her experience, the business sector was 'gagging to be quoted'. Personal interview, April 2010.
[104] Presentation at RISJ/ECI seminar, Oxford, 26 Feb. 2010.

2. There was about three times as much coverage in the broadsheet press as there was in the 'tabloid' press.

3. The science of climate change represented a low percentage within each article. Only 9% of the 427 articles monitored had more than half of the article dedicated to discussing the science. Nearly 80% had less than 10%.

4. Scientists from universities or research centres represented 12% of all those quoted on the science. This was just 1% more than NGOs, equivalent to three occasions. However, it should be stressed that these figures were influenced by the fact the NGOs were mostly to be found in just 2 of the 24 newspapers surveyed – the *Times of India* and the UK *Guardian*.

5. Very few climate sceptics were quoted, and when they were, it was in the Western press.

6. Scientists were very seldom quoted at the end of the conference, whereas NGOs were out in force.

5. Chasing the Pack

NGOs – too much of a good thing?

Some of the conclusions reached at the end of Chapter 4 merit further discussion. The first is the degree to which NGOs were quoted in the media we surveyed. The sample of our survey was relatively small (427 articles), restricted to six days and focused on who was quoted on the science.[105] However, other studies suggest that NGOs generally enjoy a strong presence in the media around the world when COP summits are being covered. For example, the more comprehensive study of media coverage of Copenhagen by the MediaClimate project showed too that civil society (mainly NGOs) represented 23% of the voices quoted, compared to 15% for 'science and expertise'.[106] (See Figure 5.1.)

The highest sector quoted was national political actors, which has some parallels with our results in Figures 4.3 and 4.4. It seems that, as the researchers point out, 'journalism and journalists follow (and monitor) power and the powerful'.

The MediaClimate study included the sectors quoted by the media on *any* topic, not just the science, so it is not directly comparable. However, a similar picture emerged from a previous study the same researchers had carried out of the Bali summit in 2007. They found that NGOs were one of the most quoted sectors there too, and were quoted significantly more than scientists and the business sectors.

This research concluded that, in the 12 countries studied, NGOs and citizens represented between 16 and 35% of the voices quoted during and after the Bali summit, national scientists and experts between 0 and 18%, and

---

[105] It is also worth pointing out that our survey did not include 13 Dec., the day when there were many demonstrations in Copenhagen in favour of an ambitious deal. NGO voices would have been widely quoted on that day.
[106] Eide et al., 'Domesticating a Global Moment', p. 10.

international scientists between 0 and 9%. The study found that:

- 'The relative strength of scientists (both national and international) varies a lot, but given the scientific nature of the problem, their role seems small.'

- 'Journalists cover equally enthusiastically NGO-actors from their home country as from foreign countries.'

- In contrast, 'business actors are very much absent from the whole coverage'.[107]

Does it *matter* that NGOs are so widely quoted? It should be of some concern that, despite the limitations of our survey, NGOs were quoted only marginally less than university scientists on the science (11 versus 12%). After all, the main error in the 2007 IPCC AR4 report which led to such a media frenzy

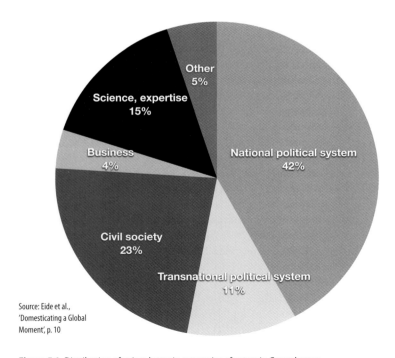

Source: Eide et al., 'Domesticating a Global Moment', p. 10

Figure 5.1. Distribution of voices by main categories of actors in Copenhagen

[107] Eide, Kunelius, and Kumpu, 'Blame, Domestication and Elite Perspectives in Global Media Culture', paper presented to the Global Dialogue Conference, Arhus, Nov. 2009, pp. 12 ff.

of criticism was based on a report by an NGO. The suggestion reported by the IPCC that the ice on the Himalayas could disappear as early as 2035 drew on what is generally known as 'grey literature' which has not been peer-reviewed, and in this case on a report by the Indian branch of an NGO, the WWF, entitled 'An Overview of Glaciers, Glacier Retreat, and Subsequent Impacts in Nepal, India and China'. The WWF report was in turn based on an article in the *New Scientist* which had quoted an Indian scientist named Syed Hasnain.[108] The IPCC has since admitted its mistake.

This is not to deny that some highly respected scientists work for NGOs, and write very solidly researched reports for them. Indeed, a second supposed 'error' in the IPCC AR4 report, again highlighted by the *Sunday Times*, was also based on a report by the WWF, this time about the Amazon's vulnerability to climate change. However, in this instance, the 'error' was incorrect sourcing rather than incorrect science. The *Sunday Times* was forced to publish an apology, including recognition of the status of the two researchers who wrote the report.[109] Indeed, many observers make the point that some NGOs are much more serious than others in presenting sound technical reports rooted in evidence and climate science, which rightly feed into the debate and the UN process. But the point here is rather that, at a time of declining public belief in the validity of climate science, some journalists would perhaps be wise to scrutinise these reports and NGO quotes more when they are dealing with the science.

A linked issue is the distribution of quotes at the end of the summit. As already mentioned, the numbers of civil society representations were severely restricted at the Bella Centre during the last days of the summit but NGOs managed to get a lot of presence in the media. Again, does it matter that NGOs were widely quoted? Many would argue that they should be welcomed as they are entirely legitimate voices with opinions that readers and viewers in most countries would be interested in knowing. Indeed, many observers would say that they are a much more legitimate voice than scientists who should stick to the science and leave policy to governments and civil society. Indeed, some climate scientists have often been accused of crossing the barriers of science and engaging in too much advocacy. But there are two countervailing arguments to this view.

The first is that the large number of NGOs quoted at the end of summit contributed hugely to the predominantly negative media reaction to the Copenhagen Accord signed by Brazil, the USA, China, India and South

[108] Jonathan Leake and Chris Hastings, 'World Misled over Himalayan Glacier Meltdown', *Sunday Times* (17 Jan. 2010): www.timesonline.co.uk/tol/news/environment/article6991177.ece. For an account of how the story came out first see Curtis Brainard, 'Q and A: Covering the IPCC', *Columbia Journalism Review* (14 Sept. 2010).

[109] Roy Greenslade, 'Sunday Times Apologises for False Climate Story in a "Correction"', Greenslade blog, 21 June 2010: www.guardian.co.uk/media/greenslade/2010/jun/21/sundaytimes-scienceofclimatechange.

Africa. Few of the NGOs, if any, held a positive view of the outcome. Indeed, the prevailing view of immense disappointment contrasted sharply with the atmosphere of a sense of hope at the start of the summit, which was in part created by the strong voice of the NGOs.

Some eminent observers, including Sir David King, the former chief scientific adviser to the British government, have argued that both the media and NGOs were major factors in the Accord being dismissed as a disaster, even though there were some positive elements within it. The Accord set no legally binding targets and bypassed the UN negotiating procedure, but some observers felt it did at least recognise a two-degree limit for temperature rises and represented the first time the USA and some large developing countries had entered into a joint agreement on the need to reduce GHG emissions.[110]

Sir David King argues that:

> *The objectives of the Copenhagen meeting were very ill-served both by the media and the NGOs. The Guardian for example leaked the draft text of the agreement drawn up by the Danish government. The NGOs were competing with each other for membership. Many of them perceive the best way forward is to be more radical than anyone else. I think [Copenhagen] became a circus as a result of both of these activities. The focus down to allowing heads of state and others to produce something useful was lost in that whole circus process. [111]*

Fiona Harvey, the *FT* environment correspondent, holds a similar view on the negative influence of the NGOs. She has labelled the role they played in Copenhagen as 'exceptionally destructive' for 'fomenting discord among developing nations' and for 'their rejection of all compromises [which] provided a cover for those governments with a vested interest in the talks' failure'. She named Greenpeace, Friends of the Earth and Oxfam as particularly at fault.[112] She points to the enormous influence they wield over journalists, and particularly those who are covering summits for the first time. Their constant emails, their physical presence, and their daily press conferences, she says, all contribute to this.[113]

Few journalists have been as open as Fiona Harvey in their complaints

---

[110] One view of the 'mistakes' the media made in representing the outcome, written shortly after the end of the summit, was published on the website Grist, which was an experiment in digital collective journalism at Copenhagen. Sam Hummel, '5 Common Mistakes in the Coverage of the Copenhagen Accord', Grist, 22 Dec. 2009, www.grist.org/article/2009-12-22-5-fallacies-in-the-coverage-of-the-copenhagen-accord.

[111] Author interview, Oxford, June 2010.

[112] Fiona Harvey, 'Green is the Colour of Climate Discord', *Financial Times* (28 Jan. 2010).

[113] Author interview, London, April 2010.

about NGOs, and many would disagree with her. But John Broder, a regular reporter on climate change for the *New York Times*, has also made the point that NGOs had considerable access to the media centre in Copenhagen. '[Interest groups] can be fairly intrusive, and it cuts into my reporting time', he told the *Columbia Journalism Review*. Another journalist for the *Jakarta Post* complained that NGOs seemed to have more right of way than journalists.[114]

The counter-argument to the view that NGOs had too much influence over the negative reaction is that they were merely reflecting the legitimate disappointment of the large numbers of governments, particularly from the G-77 negotiating bloc, who felt outrage or at least considerable pique that they had been excluded from the negotiations about the Copenhagen Accord and then asked to sign up to it. In other words, the NGOs were to a large degree simply echoing the sentiments of these countries, and were not the generators of the sentiment. Moreover, many developing countries do not have well-resourced or sophisticated media operations, so NGOs can offer a helping hand.

These are important points and the issue should be debated further, but they do lead to a second issue raised about the role of NGOs: many of them, and particularly those who work in favour of poverty alleviation in developing countries, have a clear political agenda. Again there is nothing wrong with this, except that it can distort the balance of reporting, for example, when addressing the issue of who was to blame for the lack of an ambitious deal being reached at Copenhagen. Most Western NGOs direct all their fire at Western governments, and they would of course argue that their target is frequently justified. Many NGOs rarely publicly criticise the governments of developing countries for their actions at COP summits, often for the very good reason that it could jeopardise their development programmes on the ground in countries they were attacking. But this can lead to a lack of scrutiny of developing countries and the specific role that China, for example, was reported to have played in scuppering a more ambitious deal.

A report by the author Mark Lynas in the *Guardian* soon after the end of the summit argued convincingly that aid agencies like Friends of the Earth International and Christian Aid were quick to point the blame firmly at the West when 'this was the complete opposite of the truth'.[115] Based on his presence in the private negotiating room at the end of the summit, he reported that 'it was China's representative who insisted that industrialised country targets, previously agreed as an 80% cut by 2050, be taken out of the deal'. His report was corroborated by an article in May 2010 by *Der Spiegel*

---

[114] Both quoted in Betwa Sharma, 'Good COP, Bad COP', *The Observatory: Columbia Journalism Review* (22 Dec. 2009).
[115] Mark Lynas, 'How Do I Know China Wrecked the Copenhagen Deal? I was in the Room', Guardian (22 Dec. 2009).

based on the secret tape recordings of the last-minute negotiations.[116] It seems that not just the Chinese delegate but India too was standing in the way of a more ambitious agreement.

NGOs can hardly be blamed for being part of the trend in recent years of government departments, companies and civil society organisations beefing up their media and communication divisions to get their point of view across more forcefully. As a forthcoming RISJ Working Paper will point out, there has been a shift towards aid agencies moving towards 'proactive advocacy'. One result is that 'today Oxfam has 15 members in its press office – more people than the *Independent* or the *Guardian* have general reporters'.[117] Moreover, at a huge summit like Copenhagen, it is understandable that they are competing for attention from the media with other NGOs, particularly when so many of them are present in such large numbers. According to the UNFCCC figures, around 400 joined the number of observer organisations in the 12 months prior to the summit, so it is hardly surprising they strive for media prominence at a time when not just NGOs but governments and multilateral organisations are all trying to pitch their message.

But the general point here is that, for journalists, an over-reliance on their point of view can have drawbacks. It is understandable that because of the pressure of constant deadlines and the ensuing 'churnalism' (over-reliance on press releases) journalists should turn to NGOs, whose representatives are generally much more readily available and media-savvy than many other sectors present at COP summits, and particularly scientists from universities and research centres. As already pointed out in Chapter 3, Greenpeace alone had nearly twice as many media and communications officers registered at Copenhagen than all of the 200-plus universities put together. But it may be prudent to return to the old-fashioned journalistic value of weighing up what is an appropriate diversity of sources.

The paucity of the science

The second topic worthy of more discussion is point 3 of the conclusions in Chapter 4. Other studies of the extent of media coverage of the science during the Copenhagen summit corroborate our conclusion that the science received relatively short shrift. As the UN's own analysis of more than 6,000 articles in 70 countries covering the Copenhagen summit concluded:

---

[116] Tobias Rapp, Christian Schwägerl and Gerald Traufetter, 'How India and China Sabotaged the UN Climate Summit', *Der Spiegel* (5 May 2010): www.spiegel.de/international/world/0,1518,692861-2,00.html.

[117] Glenda Cooper, 'From their own Correspondent? How Closely Do the Agendas of Aid Agencies and the Media Converge, How is This Changing, and What is the Effect on Coverage of Disasters?', RISJ Working Paper, forthcoming. Oxfam has 80–90 press officers worldwide.

> *The debate over the hacked emails by climate researchers in the UK, dubbed 'climategate' by the press, was the primary driver of coverage on the climate change science. The controversy helped to increase the coverage of the science. However, there was very little coverage of climate change science beyond the disputes resulting from the leaked emails.*[118]

The UN's analysis suggested that the WMO reports mentioned in the previous chapter did help to generate some coverage about the science. But a similar conclusion about the general paucity of the science was reached by the former BBC environment correspondent, Alex Kirby, in a paper given to the RISJ/ECI seminar held in February 2010.[119] On his (admittedly cursory) review of the *Independent* newspaper in the UK, 11 of 66 stories the paper published during the Copenhagen summit, equivalent to about 16%, were about climate science. Of the 300 stories in the *Guardian*, 16 were about the science (just over 5%). The website of the Climate Change Media Partnership published 180 stories, of which 15 were about the science, equivalent to about 7%. A presentation at the same RISJ/ECI seminar by a French science journalist and researcher, Catherine Ferrieux, suggested that, of the stories written by 37 journalists she interviewed who were covering the Copenhagen summit, only 13% were about 'climate science'.[120]

The relatively low percentage of the stories dedicated to the science can be explained by a variety of factors. First and most importantly, most of the journalists did not come to Copenhagen to report on the science, but on the negotiations and the political fighting behind them. That was the point of the Copenhagen summit, and not the science. Secondly, the sheer drama of the negotiations provided easy copy. Thirdly, many of the journalists who were present at Copenhagen were not specialist science or environment journalists but general reporters with no particular expertise.[121] For a generalist, the science is a much more difficult topic to cover accurately than getting a few quotes on the process of the negotiations. Fourthly, many specialist journalists

---

[118] UN DPI internal report, p. 5.

[119] See his talk at the RISJ/ECI conference on 26 Feb. 2010: http://reutersinstitute.politics.ox.ac.uk/fileadmin/documents/Conferences/Climate_Change/Alex_Kirby__How_the_Media_Reported_Climate.pdf.

[120] She defined 'climate science' as including carbon capture and storage, sea level rises, the Arctic, the Himalayas, Climategate, the IPPC reports and the generic term 'climate science'. The figure is based on what the journalists said they had written about, rather than any content analysis. Of the 37 journalists, who came from a wide variety of media genres and mostly from developing countries, 6 said they had written nothing about the science, while 17 said science represented only between 10 and 20% of the total number of stories they sent from Copenhagen. Her presentation can be seen at www.oxfordglobalmedia.com/images/news_images/ComparingClimateChangeReportinginCopenhagen.ppt.

[121] According to the Yale Forum, a third of the reporters sent to Copenhagen did not normally cover climate change. 38% of those interviewed by Catherine Ferrieux were generalists. An Indian journalist commented at the RISJ/ECI seminar that the Indian media sent political correspondents rather than science correspondents.

had produced background pieces on the science in the run-up to the summit. Fifthly, the demands of the 24/7 news cycle were such that many journalists were under constant pressure to provide the latest twists and turns on the state of negotiations and compete with the many others doing exactly the same thing.

Alex Kirby has eloquently summed up the challenge of reporting the science from summits:[122]

> *Covering a science story – any science story – takes some time to do properly. It needs standing up, explaining, illustrating, and an independent voice. It's much quicker to update a story about a protest, or get some quotes from a good source on the latest stage in one part of the negotiations. The great thing about that sort of story is that the journalist can never be wrong: so much is going on at a COP that there is always something you can write without fear of contradiction. But don't try that with the science, or it is liable to blow up in your face.*

These factors may explain the low percentage, but do they justify it? First, a case can be made that readers needed a solid contextual background on the science to understand why the negotiations were so important. Articles that give more background context and explanation of the science can help to increase understanding of the science. One recent study of the general coverage in the Dutch and French press of climate change found that the articles they looked at included longer news pieces that offered due background information on the science. This fact, they concluded, 'may not only help the Dutch and French readers better understand global warming, but make them more certain of its existence and consequences'.[123]

The number of journalists at Copenhagen was unprecedented, as was the number of articles published in many newspapers around the world. It may have been one of the first times that many readers had come to the topic. Copenhagen provided an excellent opportunity to provide an appropriate amount of background discussion of the science to understand the importance of the negotiations. The fact that nearly 80% of the stories the journalists wrote we monitored from Copenhagen had less than 10% of the story mentioning the climate science would suggest that not much of the essential context was given. There may have been insufficient analysis that explained the link between the process of the talks and how it might have affected the future of

---

[122] Kirby (see n. 119), p. 3.
[123] Dirikx and Gelders, 'Global Warming through the Same Lens', p. 209.

the planet. For example, the political wrangling over a two-degree target for global temperature increase, which still continues, is hardly understandable without solid reference to the science.

Moreover, it can hardly be argued that the narrative of the negotiations was so compelling that it left little space for discussing or reporting the science. Most of the print media have an online presence and, as previously mentioned, websites provide more space for the science and scientists to be included in any coverage.[124]

A second factor to bear in mind is how much 'new' science there was to report at Copenhagen. It is often maintained that, compared to the Bali summit which coincided with the year of the 2007 IPCC reports, there was significantly less science to report. Moreover, several new reports had been released at a special conference on the science held in Copenhagen in March, organised by 10 universities and attended by 2,000 climate scientists and 190 journalists.[125] In September, UNEP issued an IPCC-like report called *Climate Change Science Compendium 2009,* which, although not peer-reviewed like the IPCC assessments, was intended to give an urgent call for action due to the pace and scale of climate change since the 2007 IPCC reports.[126]

Despite this, there were still several new reports on the science from highly reputable international organisations which were made public at or during the summit. Box 5.1 gives a partial list.

In particular, the EPA's warning on 7 December, known as the 'endangerment finding', was significant for several reasons and not least because it gave the EPA the legal power to regulate the USA's major emitters of GHGs (although the Obama administration has repeatedly said it would prefer Congress to pass legislation to regulate emissions). But according to the *Columbia Journalism Review,* 'few if any articles have come out analysing the endangerment finding's impact there [on the negotiations in Copenhagen]'.[127]

To be fair, some of the reports listed and released during the six days reviewed were indeed reported by some of the media. The WMO report on the hottest decade on record for example was covered in many newspapers. But even then, according to *New York Times* blogger Andy Revkin, 'it was the gulf between rich and poor nations, not the science of global warming, that dominated talks … on Tuesday as delegates fretted about different pieces of draft language for a new climate treaty circulating in the halls'.[128]

In addition, there were some – but not many – side events on the science. In

---

[124] The journalists interviewed by Catherine Ferrieux told her that web-based media are the most likely to give a lot of space to scientists.
[125] Andy Revkin, 'Copenhagen Summit Seeks Climate Action', *Dot Earth* (12 March 2009): http://dotearth. blogs.nytimes.com/2009/03/12/copenhagen-summit-seeks-climate-action.
[126] Kerr, 'Climate Change: Amid Worrisome Signs', *Science* (13 Nov. 2009).
[127] Brainard and Russell, 'Copenhagen Watch: Disarray in Denmark?'
[128] Ibid.

Box 5.1 Science Reports during Copenhagen

7 Dec.	The EPA says officially that CO2 is a danger to human health (press conference in Copenhagen)
7 Dec.	A report from the UK government's committee on climate change on aviation (UK only)
8 Dec.	A statement from the WMO and the UK Met Office stating that the last decade had been the warmest since instrumental record-keeping began in the 1850s (press conference and side event in Copenhagen)
8 Dec.	A 2010 climate change risk index released by the NGO German Watch (press conference and side event)
9 Dec.	Release of the International Geosphere-Biosphere Programme (IGBP) climate change index, which integrates data on various indicators of climate change including CO2 levels and temperature and sea-level rises
10 Dec.	Emissions of some GHGs are higher than reported by companies and countries – details presented at the summit by Professor Ray Weiss of the Scripps Institution of Oceanography
14 Dec.	'Oceans Day' meeting on the dangers of ocean acidification organised by Stanford University and Scripps Institution (side event)
14 Dec.	Latest disaster figures released by UNISDR, UNDP and WMO (press conference)
16 Dec.	The contribution of climate change to migration and displacement given by the International Organisation for Migration (press conference)
17 Dec.	Protecting health from climate change – press conference given by the WHO
17 Dec.	Leaked UN document shows emission cuts offered would still lead to a 3 degree rise

general these were poorly attended, in contrast to the heavily populated news conferences given by the negotiating teams. For example, very few journalists attended the launch on 16 December of a seminal report by the UN's Economic Commission for Latin America on the possibly drastic effects of temperature rises on the economies of Latin America, known as the mini-Stern Report.[129] No more than 5 of the 172 journalists registered for Copenhagen from Latin America were present at the event.[130]

The French researcher, Catherine Ferrieux, recounted how two French climatologists turned up at a side event on the Mediterranean climate to find three people in the audience. Their event on sea-level rises and Arctic ice melt

[129] James Painter, 'CEPAL habla de duro impacto económico', bbcmundo, 16 Dec. 2009: www.bbc.co.uk/mundo/ciencia_tecnologia/2009/12/091216_1841_cepal_cambio_climatico_jrg.shtmlbbcmundo.
[130] Author's personal experience.

went ahead with an audience of 30, but only after lot of effort to publicise it.[131]

A similar experience was recounted by Ben Block, an NGO representative and correspondent for Worldwatch Institute's online news service. He attended several newsworthy off-the-record briefings and side events 'where no press were in sight'.[132] He was witness to 'reporters [who] travel in packs, follow the back-and-forth negotiations, and overlook more difficult stories on issues such as adaptation, indigenous peoples' rights, and technology'.

This 'travelling in packs' to follow the minutiae of the negotiations does seem to have been a common phenomenon at the Bella Centre. As the BBC internet environment correspondent Richard Black has explained, part of the problem was that very few journalists really knew what was going on. This made reporting a 'nightmare'. As Black wrote at the time:[133]

> In smaller gatherings that I've reported on … you feel
> reasonably confident of having a line on everything
> important that's going on. Not here; it's impossible. Some
> journalist somewhere knows something you don't, you can
> guarantee that; and you just hope it's not more important
> than the thing you know that they don't.

Black added that reporting became even more difficult after the heads of state arrived in the second week, as journalists 'worked in even more of an information deficit than previously', due in part to the enormous amount of spin put on the negotiations.[134] The result was that many of the journalists – overworked, stressed out and keen not to be outdone by their rivals – hyped the story of the negotiations, when really the only angle on that story that mattered was what happened at the end of the conference: did the negotiators reach an agreement, and if so, what sort of agreement was it?

It is hard not to agree with Dr Max Boykoff of the University of Colorado at Boulder that the stories out of Copenhagen mostly reflected 'classic journalism norms of drama'.[135] He and other scholars have pointed out that the media need strong elements of not just drama, but novelty too. Copenhagen provided the new and exciting drama, but in the balance between reporting the drama and giving the context necessary for the story, there was little doubt which journalists chose to report on. The coverage of the summit may turn out to be another example of what Boykoff has called the 'episodic framing of

---

[131] Communication with the author, March 2010.
[132] Block, 'Covering Climate Change'.
[133] Richard Black, 'COP15 Copenhagen Climate Summit: Day 4', BBC website, 10 Dec. 2009: www.bbc.co.uk/blogs/thereporters/richardblack/2009/12/cop15_copenhagen_climate_summi_2.html.
[134] Richard Black, 'COP15: Titanic Nears the Harbour', BBC website, 16 Dec. 2009: www.bbc.co.uk/blogs/thereporters/richardblack/2009/12/cop15_titanic_nears_the_harbou.html.
[135] Quoted in Block, 'Covering Climate Change'.

news', rather than 'thematic framing' whereby stories are situated in a larger thematic context.[136]

The study by the MediaClimate project came to a similar conclusion about the emphasis on the political drama of Copenhagen and the little attention paid to climate change, even in comparison with the Bali summit:[137]

> *Stories particularly about the summit overshadowed clearly stories that would focus on climate change more generally. Given the nature of the summit as a news event this is not surprising, but with some comparisons to Bali, it becomes a bit more interesting. As a rule, coverage of Copenhagen was more focused on the summit itself. Thus, although it is customary in journalism during such heightened moments of official agenda attention to also invest more to other stories related to the item. In Copenhagen, the resources in newsrooms were directed to following the summit itself. Copenhagen summit provoked less 'side-coverage' than Bali.*

It is understandable that the voracious demands of the 24/7 news websites and TV channels made it virtually impossible to resist the urge to give regular updates on the negotiations. But one wonders about the extent to which the constant images of negotiators – often 'men in grey suits' – remained appealing to audiences around the world. The MediaClimate study, although of print media, showed a 'huge male dominance of voices' quoted throughout the summit.[138] It ranged from 70% male voices in Finland to between 90 and 100% in Canada, Israel, Russia, Bangladesh, Pakistan, Egypt and China.

It is also apposite to note that a BBC-commissioned audience survey of the cross-media BBC coverage of the summit, which was rated the best for news on Copenhagen, showed that it had 'low engagement amongst the audience' in the UK.[139] Only 25% of those surveyed claimed to have followed the story closely (significantly below the average of 38% for 'big stories'). There was also a perceived lack of importance around the story, both for audiences personally (14% consider it very important for them) and as citizens (19%). The authors of the survey suggested this may 'have been the result of audiences not fully understanding it, with BBC possibly not helping to improve audience understanding as much as with other stories (56% versus the Big Story average of 67%)'.

---

[136] Maxwell T. Boykoff and Jules M. Boykoff, 'Climate Change and Journalistic Norms: A Case-Study of US Mass-Media Coverage', *Geoforum*, 38 (2007).
[137] Eide et al., 'Domesticating a Global Moment', p. 9.
[138] Ibid., p. 13.
[139] Mark Donavan, 'Audience Feedback on the BBC News Coverage of the Copenhagen Summit', Jan. 2010: www.audiencesportal.com/article_list/news__journalism_articles/bbc_news_copenhagen_summit.aspx

Even the journalists with less demanding deadlines did not seem to have stepped back much from the ephemeral nature of the negotiations and the men in suits, and spent more time discussing the more durable essence of the science. This last point is reinforced by the fact that, as already discussed in Chapter 3, a large number of scientists from universities and other reputable research institutions were present – and yet very few of them were quoted. There were all sorts of good explanations for this: their numbers were severely restricted in the second week of the conference; some may have wanted to keep a low profile in the aftermath of 'Climategate', whilst others may have felt that Copenhagen was not about the science; it may have been the lack of an effective press department, or the lack of a central area for the media to locate scientists willing to speak to the media or a general lack of interest in them on the part of journalists. It may have been the few side events or press events organised by the university scientists there. But it was certainly the case that at a period in which media coverage of climate change reached a historical peak in many countries, the scientific imperative was a dim echo rarely heard above the din of chattering negotiators – and the journalists feeding off them.

6. The Urge to Communicate

The previous two chapters have showed that, for several reasons, the journalists at Copenhagen chose not to include much reporting of climate science, which simply could not compete with the novelty, the drama and the power politics of the negotiations. One factor that could have helped – the presence of many scientists, and particularly those from universities, at the summit – did not seem to contribute to overcoming the perennial challenge of getting the science into mainstream news coverage. If it is the case that many journalists opted not to cover the science when the peg and the opportunity were self-evident, then how much more difficult will it be to find interesting, new and engaging ways to report on it when all the traditional obstacles described in Chapter 2 return? Climate science, like most science, remains a complex topic to maintain the attention of editors and the general public alike. Indeed, after Copenhagen the challenge if anything has become greater: there is strong evidence to suggest that in the developed world, after the summit the amount of coverage of climate change plummeted to 2006 levels in part due to 'climate fatigue'. (See Figure 2.1 above.)

The debate about how journalists and scientists should be involved in more, different or better communication with the public has been around for several years. In part this has been driven by concerns about poor science literacy around the world. Even in the USA, a recent survey found that four in ten adults could not name a fossil fuel, five in ten think nuclear energy causes global warming, and six in ten cannot name a renewable energy source.[140] But the debate became even more pressing in early 2010. A sequence of events starting towards the end of 2009 created a winter of discontent – at least in the northern hemisphere – for climate scientists and many of the journalists who follow their work. It provoked a healthy flurry of attention by the media, the science community, the NGOs and governing classes, not just on the robustness of climate science but also on the way forward for communicating it.

---

[140] Lloyd and Russell, 'Better Communication Begets Trust', *Columbia Journalism Review* (23 Feb. 2010).

It is not the purpose of this chapter to revisit the three main developments which provided the context for the debate: the posting on the internet of more than 1,000 confidential emails from the Climatic Research Unit (CRU) at the University of East Anglia; the revelation of at least one important error in the 2007 IPCC reports; and (much less so) the failure of the Copenhagen summit to achieve a binding, ambitious, legally binding treaty on GHG emission reductions.

But climate scientists were clearly prompted by the UEA emails and the IPCC errors to re-examine how they should communicate their science. Websites, particularly in the USA, buzz with the debate.[141] More openness, more transparency, more explanation of risk and uncertainty, more debating with serious sceptics online or off, and even the employment of public relations companies have all been strongly advocated. There seems to be a consensus too there should be more or different engagement with the public, either directly or through the media. It was remarkable how in the early months of 2010 many prominent scientists, particularly in the UK and the USA, publicly stressed the need to communicate more or better with the media and public in the future. (See the quotes in Box 6.1.)

However, there has been less debate about the details of the way this engagement might take place. Traditional or innovatory forms? Top–down or participatory? New media or old? Less news but more features, soap operas and drama? All scientists or the best communicators? This last question has prompted a re-examination of the degree to which climate scientists around the world are themselves an obstacle to better coverage in the media: to what extent are they willing to engage with the media and to respond adequately to the increased demand on their time; and do they have the skill base and necessary media training to communicate well? At the very least a 'good climate science performer', particularly on broadcast media, needs (a) to know the relevant area of climate science well, (b) to be able to communicate it well and succinctly, and (c) have a thick enough skin to ward off the inevitable personal attacks from climate sceptics once they stick their heads above the parapet. Many scientists are unsurprisingly wary of jeopardising their careers or the respect from their key peer group (usually other scientists), by being seen to say something unwise or simplistic or by having their views misrepresented. For many, it is an area they would much prefer not to enter.

However, the greatest challenge for climate reporters and scientists alike remains how to make climate science a sustained part of the editorial agenda. In common with other important, complex and slow-burn issues, it has proved difficult to convey its importance and engage the interest of editors and a wider

---

[141] Some of the best discussions can be found at the *Observatory* published by the Columbia Journalism Review (http://www.cjr.org/the_observatory/), the Yale Forum on Climate Change and the Media (http://www.yaleclimatemediaforum.org) and the blog http://climateprogress.org.

Box 6.1: The Engagement Imperative

Lord Nick Stern, author the Stern Report: 'I do think communication is fundamental. I think that scientists and social scientists are not trained generally in the communication of policy, particularly about the management of risk which is about the most difficult thing to communicate on that there is. And so we have to get better at it, and we have to think about how to get better at it. We are dependent on the media, and on responsible, thoughtful, reporting of the issues. Reflection, analysis in the newspapers, on the TV, and on the net is very important. We have to help the media do what it does better and that it is quite a hard thing to do because the pressures now are on shock, horror and speed ... You have to get people to think quietly and ponder and that's a difficult thing to do.' (LSE, 10 March 2010)

Professor Bob Watson, chief scientific adviser to Defra (UK): 'We need the media desperately to be the mediator [between us and the public]. As scientists we must communicate better, and say what we know as well as what we don't know.' (SMC event, London, 31 March 2010)

Lord Martin Rees, president of the Royal Society (UK): 'There's less demarcation between experts and laypersons. Campaigners and bloggers enrich the debate. But professionals have special obligations to engage.' (First Reith Lecture, 1 June 2010)

Sir David King, former chief scientific adviser to the UK government: 'The scientific community are now battered and standing back, saying who's going to put their head above the parapet? We've got to have a nucleus of people that can communicate. I do think we need to be nurturing spokespeople for the media from within the scientific community.' (Author interview, June 2010)

Sir John Houghton, former chair of the IPCC: 'We are losing that war [public relations with the sceptics] because we're not good at PR. Your average scientist is not a good PR person because he wants to get on with his science.' (BBC Wales, 12 February 2010)

Professor Ralph Cicerone, president of the National Academy of Sciences, USA: 'We are not doing a very good job of translating what we are doing.' (February 2010)

Professor Jane Lubchenco, director of NOAA, USA: 'Scientists have seriously underestimated the importance of explaining what we know about climate in a way people can understand.' (March 2010)

---

audience in a media age often dominated by news about celebrities, crime, and sport – in short, the challenge is to 'make the significant interesting'. This is made all the more difficult by the newsroom cuts in many privately owned Western media, the decline in resources for overseas reporting and long-format reporting, and the reduction in specialist science reporters in some countries.

It is even more of a challenge for the popular or tabloid media. As we saw in Chapter 4, tabloid coverage of climate change is of considerably lower volume than that of the broadsheet press. It would probably also be true of the Millennium Development Goals, nuclear weaponry, peak oil, the threats to biodiversity, and many other urgent challenges of the twenty-first century (although climate change and nuclear proliferation are probably the two with the most potentially disastrous consequences). There is a real danger that well-trained and knowledgeable journalists working for *The Economist*, the *FT* and the *Guardian* continue to speak to a small and elite audience, at least in global terms. But the audience for complex subjects does not have to remain small.

For example, the most read newspaper in the UK, the *Sun*, has shown with its first ever appointment of an environment editor, Ben Jackson, in March 2009 that it is possible to reach a regular and wider readership on climate change and the environment. Jackson gives the example of a *Sun* driver who spoke to him recently about the Medieval Warm Period – 'something that would not have happened six months ago'.[142] He says it has been more difficult to get climate science stories in the paper in 2010 as there are no political developments to anticipate like Copenhagen in 2009. But he has managed to do on-the-spot reporting about deforestation in Acre in the Amazon, several stories about the changing climate affecting wildlife and bio-diversity, and features on what private enterprise is doing such as the new generation of electric cars. '*Sun* readers are interested in developments that affect their lives', he says.[143]

Space does not allow here a fuller discussion of the much-debated broader issue for climate scientists or advocates of how best to communicate science, whether it is through popular or elite media. Suffice it to say that books like Professor Mike Hulme's *Why we Disagree about Climate Change* have done a very useful job of clearly outlining the dilemmas. For example, Professor Hulme rightly draws attention to the limitations of what is known as the 'deficit model' of science communication. [144] In essence, this is the idea that, if only climate scientists could communicate better by shouting louder or in a different way, the public and the media would somehow 'get the science' and combat the problem. He points out the advantages of shifting from a 'deficit' to a 'dialogue' model and the importance of 'cultural circuits' through which information about climate change is processed.

These are important debates. However, it is clear that mainstream media and their interaction with climate scientists will remain part of the mix that shapes public opinion and understanding. In order to get a sense of the current state of this interaction from both a UK and international perspective, we sent out questionnaires to around 40 environment journalists and 40 climate scientists around the world (of whom 54 replied). We wanted to have a snapshot – it can be no more than that – of the relationship between the two communities. We looked specifically at how they saw their recent experience of each other and, when it was poor, what were the reasons for it; and what were their main recommendations to each other for improving each others' work in the future. We also examined whether there were important differences between the West

---

[142] Ben Jackson speaking at the RISJ/ECI public event in Oxford, 26 Feb. 2010. Climate sceptics stress the significance of the Medieval Warm Period because it cannot have been caused by GHGs.
[143] Author interview, Sept. 2010.
[144] Mike Hulme, *Why we Disagree about Climate Change* (2009), ch. 7.

(UK, USA, Italy and Australia) where climate sceptic voices have been heard loudly, and other countries where they have had much less of a presence.

We end the chapter by drawing on the answers to the survey, and other initiatives and proposals around the world to describe eight ideas which might help both climate scientists and the media to improve the coverage and possibly, engage the public better.

Doubting the science

The media's coverage of the UEA emails and the IPCC errors do seem to have combined with the record-breaking cold winters in some Western countries to shift significantly public attitudes there about the seriousness or certainty with which the general public held the science of climate change. Several opinion polls carried out in early 2010 in the USA and UK mapped a decline in public belief that global warming is happening, and that it is human-caused. For example, in July the George Mason University Center for Climate Change Communication concluded on the basis of a survey of around 1,000 respondents carried out in December 2009 and January 2010 that:[145]

- In 2008, 71% of Americans said 'yes', global warming is happening. By 2010, however, this number had dropped significantly to 57%.

- In 2008, more than half of Americans (57%) said human activities were causing global warming. By 2010, however, this had dropped 10 points to 47%.

- A 9-point drop since autumn 2008 in public trust in scientists as a source of information about global warming.

Only 29% of those surveyed had heard of 'Climategate', but of those who had nearly half said it had made them 'somewhat' or 'much more certain' that global warming is *not* happening. The researchers concluded that the survey results strongly suggested that 'Climategate' had a significant effect on public beliefs in global warming and trust in scientists. The loss of trust in scientists, however, was primarily among people with a 'strongly individualistic worldview or politically conservative ideology'.

Similarly, a widely quoted BBC poll published in February 2010 found that

---

[145] A. A. Leiserowitz, E. W. Maibach, C. Roser-Renouf, N. Smith, E. Dawson, *Climategate, Public Opinion, and the Loss of Trust*, George Mason University Center for Climate Change Communication, July 2010: www.climatechangecommunication.org/images/files/Climategate_Public%20Opinion_and%20Loss%20of%20Trust%281%29.pdf.

25% of the 1,000 adults polled in the UK did not think global warming was happening, an increase of 10% since a similar poll was conducted in November 2009.[146] In this case however, it was not so clear what role 'Climategate' had played. The poll suggested that of those who had heard of news stories about 'flaws or weaknesses in climate science' (more than 50%), 16% said they were now *more* convinced of the risks of climate change, against only 11% who were less convinced.[147] Richard Black, the BBC internet environment correspondent, is not the only analyst to suggest that people's immediate experience of the weather may be a stronger determinant of changes in attitudes towards climate change.[148]

It is more difficult to assess the effect 'Climategate' has had on attitudes in non-Western countries as few polls have been carried out.[149] The May 2010 Synovate/Deutsche Welle poll of 13,000 people in 18 countries suggested that the number of people 'very concerned' about climate change remained pretty constant at 30% (compared to 29% in 2009 and 30% in 2008).[150] However, there was a small increase in the total percentage of people who were not concerned about climate change at all because they believed it was just part of a natural cycle of events. Of those surveyed in 2010 9%, compared to 4% in 2008, were not worried. The researchers said that there was 'no doubt [this figure was] at least partially influenced by the several groups who have questioned the validity of the concerns around climate change over the past year'.

It is doubtful that most people in developing countries have even heard of 'Climategate', as the media there have scarcely reported it. In China, for example, some newspapers copied and published reports in the Western media but they did not investigate or report on 'Climategate' directly. Indeed, as the Synovate/Deutsche Welle poll indicated, the number of people in China who said they were very concerned about climate change had increased from 26% in 2007 to 58% in 2010.

Whatever the exact drivers of the decline in public belief in global warming and trust in climate scientists, it is pretty clear that both took a dip in the early months of 2010 in the USA and the UK. However, there was evidence

---

[146] 'Climate Scepticism "On the Rise", BBC Poll Shows', BBC website, 7 Feb. 2010: http://news.bbc.co.uk/1/hi/8500443.stm.

[147] Richard Black, 'Rising Scepticism: A Chill Wind?', BBC website, 5 Feb. 2010: www.bbc.co.uk/blogs/thereporters/richardblack/2010/02/cold_view_of_rising_scepticism.html.

[148] See also Damian Carrington, 'Slide in Climate Change Belief is a Temporary Glitch', Guardian website, 12 March 2001: www.guardian.co.uk/environment/blog/2010/mar/12/climate-change-belief-polls.

[149] The Dec. 2009 BBC World Service/Globescan survey of 24,000 people in 23 countries concluded that public concern about climate change was 'at its highest level since Globescan began international tracking in 1998'. But the survey was conducted between June and Oct. of that year, before the questioning of climate science really took hold.

[150] Details can be found at: www.synovate.com/news/article/2010/05/climate-change-concern-remains-high-across-the-globe-says-synovate-and-deutsche-welle-global-study.html.

from surveys later in the year that there was a slight rebound in the US, as memories of the extreme cold weather and the scandals subsided.[151]

The impact on journalists

What is less well-known is the profound effect that 'Climategate' had on the way several editors and environment journalists in the mainstream media perceived the reporting of climate change. As part of her research carried out in May to June 2010, RISJ journalist fellow Margot O'Neill interviewed or took comments at public forums from ten British journalists in mainstream broadcast, print and online journalism. All of them have specialised, or are specialising, in environmental reporting. She found that:[152]

- Half of the journalists described 'Climategate' as a *game changer* in their reporting of climate change. It was described variously as 'seminal', 'a massive turning point for all of us', 'a defining moment in our careers', 'a big turning point', and as creating a 'new mood afoot in newsrooms'.

- Half also believed they or their media organisations *missed the story* or took too long to cover it: 'We missed its significance', 'we were not quick enough', 'the BBC did miss it' and 'we ignored Climategate for too long'.

- When asked about the significance of 'Climategate', most described it as *exposing the imperfect nature of the scientific process*: 'scientists are not squeaky clean', or 'it threw into stark relief the way science worked'.

- Four journalists spoke about its *effect on their editors*: 'most are sceptical anyway and they saw this as a chance to give sceptics a good airing', 'many editors are sceptical and saw this as proof that we'd gone native', 'we had to defend the science in editorial meetings', and 'editors said the science was now being challenged'.

- Many journalists said it was *hard now to generate interest in climate change stories* mainly due to fatigue with the story

---

[151] 'American Opinion on Climate Change Warms Up', ScienceDaily, 8 June 2010: www.sciencedaily.com/releases/2010/06/100608151052.htm.
[152] Margot O'Neill, 'Climate Change Reporting: A Stormy Forecast', RISJ journalist fellowship paper, Trinity Term 2010, forthcoming.

but that 'Climategate' stories were popular with editors and the public.

- Half said they were either *giving sceptics more coverage* since 'Climategate' or were more open to their points of view: 'I am now more inclined to include sceptics', 'I don't use them more often but I am more willing to consider what they have to say', and 'Maybe we should have engaged more credible sceptics earlier'.

- Two journalists spoke about *specific changes* to how their reports were worded: 'I will no longer say that "the vast majority of scientists" but "establishment scientists" believe in man-made global warming'.

These quotes were taken before the Muir Russell review of the UEA emails concluded in July 2010 that it had 'not found any evidence of behaviour that might undermine the conclusions of the IPCC assessments' – in other words, climate science remained essentially robust.[153] It is not known what effect this report and a series of others which have essentially defended climate science will have on the media, and editors in particular. What is certainly the case is that many editors did see 'Climategate' as a chance to reflect more what the public was telling them. As Greenpeace UK's Joss Garman wrote in February 2010,[154]

> one extremely influential British journalist told me that editors are coming under significant pressure to adopt a more contrarian stance ... because they are receiving scores of emails and telephone calls daily from the public demanding a more sceptical line. They are receiving very few messages supporting the consensus scientific view.

Blame game

Another fall-out of 'Climategate' and the questioning of the IPCC reports has been something of a blame game between journalists and climate scientists, at least in the UK. Speaking at a RSIJ/ECI event in February 2010, Fiona Harvey of the *Financial Times* laid into scientists for 'at first reacting disastrously to the UEA emails, claiming the important thing was that they had been stolen.

---

[153] The full text of the Muir Russell review can be found at: www.guardian.co.uk/environment/2010/jul/07/findings-muir-russell-review.
[154] Joss Garman, 'Climate Scientists are Losing Ground Against Deniers' Disinformation', 15 Feb. 2010: www.guardian.co.uk/environment/cif-green/2010/feb/15/climate-science-ipcc-sceptics.

They just did not understand that no one cared whether they had been stolen or not, just as with the MPs' expenses.' She and many others have in private and in public strongly criticised the UEA and the IPCC for their slow and inadequate media responses (see Box 6.2). They complained that the scientists just did not make themselves available to answer questions on the 'scandals'.[155] The British journalist Fred Pearce has called the response to the UEA emails 'a public relations disaster' and quoted an unnamed PR expert as saying it should be taught in university communication courses as an example of how not to respond.[156] Some journalists – but by no means all – felt that when the scientists in the UK did eventually speak publicly, they should have come out more robustly to counter the sceptics, rather than just restricting their comments to the science.[157]

For their part, some climate scientists have complained bitterly that the extensive coverage of 'Climategate', and particularly that of the *Guardian* in the UK, was out of all proportion to its significance for the science of climate change. Typical has been Oxford University's Myles Allen who lambasted the media after the Muir Russell report exonerated the UEA of fiddling the science. He commented:

> *What everyone has lost sight of is the spectacular failure of*
> *mainstream journalism to keep the whole affair in perspective.*
> *... Yet the only error in the actual data used for climate*
> *change detection to have emerged from this whole affair*
> *amounted to a few hundredths of a degree in the estimated*
> *global temperature of a couple of years in the late 1870s.[158]*

It was a view echoed in the USA by Gavin Schmidt of NASA in New York, who argued that 'the implications of climate science are too important for all of the media oxygen to be taken up by non-issues'.[159]

Another line of attack from scientists has been the amount of airtime and space given to sceptics in the mainstream media after a period of relative absence. This, they say, is 'false balance' or a 'bias of balance' as it gives equal footing to the sceptics who represent a minority view. A February 2010 report from Fairness and Accuracy in Reporting (FAIR) in the USA criticised the

---

[155] E.g. Tom Clarke, the Channel 4 science correspondent, has spoken of the 'significant vacuum' left by scientists at the time of the UEA emails.

[156] Pearce, *Climate Files*, pp. 179 ff.

[157] See the SMC director Fiona Fox's blog on a SMC press briefing in London, 'Thoughts on "Climategate"', On Science and the Media, 9 Feb. 2010: fionafox.blogspot.com/2010/02/thoughts-on-climategate.html.

[158] '"Climategate" Review: Verdict', *Guardian* (7 July 2010): www.guardian.co.uk/ commentisfree/cif-green/2010/jul/07/climategate-review-expert-verdict. See too Myles Allen's debate with Fred Pearce and others at the Royal Institute in London on 14 July 2010. An audio archive is available at www.rigb.org/content Control?action=displayEvent&id=1010.

[159] Ibid.

mainstream media there for returning to 'the bad old days of false balance'.[160] Sir David King in the UK is one of those to capture the mood:[161]

> *My personal experience with the media starts from the year 2000. What I found was that on the whole I got a very good press although it was irritating that if I was representing the voice of 3,000 scientists they would find the one scientist who disagreed with all 3,000 to oppose me. So this apparent balance of opinion actually began to disappear about 2005 or 2006; I saw a turning point. The disappointment for me is that Climategate has pushed us right back to that position. It feels like Sisyphus, we've pushed it right to the top of the hill only to allow the boulder to roll right back down again.*

Not everyone would necessarily agree with another assertion by Sir David that the media had fallen 'hook, line and sinker' for the 'superb' campaign – which he says has probably been financed and orchestrated from the USA – and carried out against the UEA and Dr Pachauri of the IPCC. But two things are clear. The first is that trust between some parts of the media and climate scientists was in need of as much rebuilding as the public's trust in climate science. And the second is now almost a truism: the media landscape in which both sectors work has been permanently revolutionised by the role of the blogosphere.

It is not, as some would argue, that 'while Fleet Street kowtowed to the green lobby, it was the climate sceptic bloggers who should be thanked for changing the climate debate'.[162] It is more that climate scientists now work in an atmosphere where their work is subject to as much scrutiny from the public, many of them bloggers, as their peers. Many of the bloggers are of a conservative ideology.[163] But there are serious and well-informed bloggers who are not driven by political ideologies or by money from the fossil fuel lobby. The blogosphere may be 'impure' compared to the peer-review process but it clearly demands openness and access to data that were absent in the pre-internet days. And it is here to stay.

---

[160] Julie Hollar, 'Climategate' Overshadows Copenhagen: Media Regress to the Bad Old Days of False Balance', FAIR, Feb. 2010: www.fair.org/index.php?page=4006. See also climate progress.org, 'How the Status Quo Media Failed on Climate Change', 29 July 2010.

[161] Author interview, Oxford, June 2010.

[162] Matt Ridley, 'The Global Warming Guerrillas', *The Spectator* (3 Feb. 2010): www.spectator.co.uk/essays/all/5749853/the-global-warming-guerrillas.thtml.

[163] Lord Anthony Giddens e.g. has frequently expressed concern that the cross-party political consensus on climate change in the UK is under threat: the top ten conservative party blogs in the UK are all sceptical of climate change. But the Conservative–Lib Deb government under David Cameron remains publicly committed to tackling climate change.

Box 6.2: The IPCC and the Media

Contrary to popular belief, since its formation in 1988 the IPCC has not actually carried out its own research on climate change. Rather, it publishes what are known as assessment reports, which summarise the state of knowledge about the science based on published or peer-reviewed scientific literature and to act as a guide to policy-makers.

Its fourth assessment reports, published in 2007, received considerable media attention around the world, not least because of the conclusion that it was 90% likely that most of the observed temperature increase since the mid-twentieth century was due to the increase in GHG concentrations caused by human activity. Many environmental journalists accepted the 2007 reports as gospel.

The problems started when critics, both in the mainstream media and in blogs, began to point out errors in the report or sections in it which overstated the level of certainty on some issues. In particular, as is well-known, much attention was paid to a claim that the Himalayan glaciers could disappear by 2035. The initial reaction from the IPCC chairman, Dr Rajendra Pachauri, was to deny the mistake even though the IPCC later admitted it.

What has received far less scrutiny is how well-equipped the IPCC is to deal with media attention. Most of the hundreds of scientists who offer their services to the IPCC do so in a voluntary manner. In fact the IPCC employs around ten salaried staff at its base in Geneva, of whom only one deals with media and communications. So lack of money and resources would seem to be the most obvious explanation why a Nobel peace prize-winning organisation, which publishes some of the most prestigious scientific reports in the world about the most pressing issue of the day, can employ only one staff media person.

Journalists have been very critical of the IPCC's response to the Himalayan glacial error. Fiona Harvey, Financial Times correspondent, describes its reaction as 'dreadful', as she had to wait two weeks for a response to her request for an official reaction. One UN insider said that a response had been drafted by UNEP, but it was delayed for several days as it had to be signed off by several members of the IPCC panel including scientists and UN officials. It is not just journalists who are critical. Professor Bob Watson said in a public debate in London in July that 'it was not the IPCC mistake that was the problem, but the IPCC's failure to admit the mistake quickly'. This inability to respond quickly to correct its mistakes probably harmed its reputation more than the original error.

Ironically, a press briefing given by one of the IPCC's vice-chairs at the UNFCCC's Bonn meeting in June 2010 provided a robust defence to journalists of the Himalayan error. Professor Jean-Pascal van Ypersele gave a clear explanation that the error was tucked away on pp. 492–3 of volume 2 of the impact report, but not in the summary for policy-makers or in the synthesis report. It was a 'very unfortunate' error, but hardly surprising given the length of all the IPCC 2007 reports (3,000 pp.). Many at the briefing wondered why such a defence could not have been mounted shortly after the error emerged.

Professor Martin Parry, who co-chaired the working group responsible for the much-criticised IPCC impact report, was initially unavailable for comment when the error about the Himalayan glaciers first emerged. However, in a brave change of heart, he formed part of a panel in London in July organised by the SMC which responded to criticisms of the IPCC reports from the Dutch Environment Agency. The reward for his courage was to receive a lot of coverage of his point of view in the British mainstream media.

As the reviews of the UEA emails and the IPCC continue to publish their results, many commentators have already pointed out that the central claims of mainstream climate change remain unchanged. But are the IPCC's communication failings as equally unchanged? The review of the IPCC carried out by the IAC included a strong recommendation that it should complete and implement a communications strategy quickly. Its sensible recommendations were:

> • More user-friendly derivative products based on assessment reports, such as a booklet that answers questions asked frequently by policy-makers, individuals sceptical about climate change and the interested public.
>
> • A FAQ section in each Working Group report.
>
> • A rapid response plan to reply, in a coordinated and timely manner and with an appropriate tone, to the criticisms and concerns that inevitably arise in such a contested arena.
>
> • Empowerment of and training for appropriate IPCC leaders to speak to the media not only about the content of the assessment reports but also the process used to generate them.
>
> But it was left open what resources and how many people were needed. Some observers pointed out the incongruence of the IPCC having one media officer at the Copenhagen summit compared to the 20 employed by Greenpeace; in contrast, the IPCC's colleagues at the UNFCCC have a permanent team of 10 media workers. There is little doubt it needs a much more agile press operation, and some would say, a rapid response unit to respond to criticisms.

Results of the Survey

From May to July of 2010, about 80 questionnaires were sent out by email, of which 40 went to environment journalists and 40 to climate scientists around the world. The text of the questionnaires can be seen in Appendices 6 and 7. To maintain some symmetry, we selected the same 12 countries we had used for the content analysis described in Chapter 4. Twenty-seven journalists and 27 scientists responded, and all 12 countries were represented, though to different degrees. Inevitably, there was a bias towards those based in the UK.[164] Of the 27 journalists, 8 were from the UK, but there was a near-equal representation from Western countries (13 from the UK, USA, Australia and Italy) and non-Western countries (14 from Brazil, China, Egypt, India, Mexico, Nigeria, Russia and Vietnam). The journalists were 'frontline' environment correspondents or journalists who regularly report on the environment. They worked in different media genres (broadcast, print and internet). The full list of respondents can be seen in Appendix 8.

The scientists were mostly climate scientists, although a few had other areas of expertise. All of them regularly engage with the media and comment on topics related to climate science. Of the 27, 16 were from Western countries (of which 8 were from the UK), and 11 non-Western. 15 of them were professors.

The survey was mainly designed to do four things:

> • To measure the perception of the two groups about the

---

[164] It was easier to chase them to fill in the questionnaires. Alister Doyle of Reuters was regarded as being from the UK, even though he is based in Oslo.

other in the period after 'Climategate' and other setbacks to the public perception of climate science.

- To get a sense of what the two groups identified as the main reasons for the poor or mediocre relationship (when they described it as such).

- To identify what the two groups saw as the three main priorities which could help the other in the coming months.

- To see if there were any major variations between the responses from Western and non-Western countries.

There are a variety of limitations to the results of the survey. The sample is not large, it is self-selecting and it is only from 12 countries. So the survey should only be seen as a snapshot, but an interesting snapshot nevertheless. The experiences of the 54 respondents were very diverse, but some common trends can still be teased out. Here are some of the main conclusions:

The state of the relationship

Despite the description above of the impact of 'Climategate' on relationships between journalists and scientists in the UK, a surprisingly high percentage of the respondents described the relationship with the other as still being 'good' or 'very good'. Of the journalists speaking of scientists, 18 (67%) said it was good or very good and nine (33%) 'OK' or 'poor'. Of the scientists speaking of journalists, a slightly lower number (17 or 63%) said the relationship was good or very good.

Of the nine journalists who described the relationship as OK or poor, four were from Western and five from the non-Western countries. However, in the case of scientists, seven of the ten who described it this way were from the West. Only two scientists and one journalist (all three from Western countries) described the relationship as poor.

Bad experience

Of the five options the journalists were given for describing an OK or poor relationship (see question 3 on the questionnaire), the three most common answers chosen were 'reluctance of scientist to comment on areas you wanted him/her to comment on' (10), 'inability of scientist to explain the science clearly and succinctly' (9) and 'lack of availability' (8).[165]

Of the eight options the scientists were given, their answers were evenly spread across all of them. However, 'lack of understanding', 'sensationalising' and 'inaccuracies' on the part of journalists were marginally the most quoted.

Three ways to improve

The scientists ranked 'more training for general journalists' and 'more journalists specialising in climate science' as the two most important (chosen 13 times each as a top three ranking), followed by 'a less adversarial framing of climate science' (11 times).[166] The three options in the list least favoured were 'more careful use of language', 'more inventiveness' and 'less doom and gloom stories'. Non-Western scientists were particularly in favour of more training (chosen 8 times) whilst 'more specialist journalists' was spread nearly equally between Western and non-Western scientists. There were significantly fewer non-Western scientists emphasising a less adversarial framing (just 3 of the 11 mentions). Again, this was perhaps an indication of climate sceptics being given less space or airtime in non-Western media.

The journalists chose 'more reports by climate scientists on topical issues' as the most popular top three option by some margin (chosen 17 times). Next came 'more availability by scientists to speak to the media' (13 times) and then 'more scientists who are prepared to debate with climate sceptics' (also 13 times). Just behind in fourth came 'more media training for scientists' (12 times). Least favoured were 'more media training for press officers at universities/research centres' and 'more presence and availability of scientists at conferences like the COP'. There was little difference in the priorities between Western and non-Western journalists. This suggests journalists all over the world are driven most by what would help them most in practical ways to report the news.

Other points

The answers to question 5 from journalists ('which organisation has dealt the best with the media in recent months') were very diverse. But it was significant to note that several Western journalists mentioned their poor experience with the UEA and the IPCC at the time of the questioning of their procedures or science. Both were criticised for their slow or inadequate response. However,

---

[165] We included the answers given to question (3) by journalists who had described their relationship as very good or good.
[166] We chose the top three rankings of all the respondents, rather than weighting all the rankings of the options. This was because several respondents chose three or less options in their responses, rather than giving a full ranking of the ten options available.

a couple of non-Western journalists did mention the IPCC as among those generally responding well to their requests.

It is worth mentioning that amongst those organisations who were mentioned more than once were UNEP, the WHO, the IIED, Oxford University and the Potsdam Institute. All of these organisations have active media or press officers.

The scientists too offered a wide range of responses to the question 'could you give an excellent example of the media's coverage of climate change in the last 12 months?' *Nature* magazine was mentioned four times, *The Economist* and the BBC twice. The *Guardian's* reporting of 'Climategate' was mentioned twice, once as a good example, one as a bad example. Many other publications, blogs and programmes were mentioned once.

Ideas for the future

Other organisations have published guidelines and practical suggestions for the media and climate scientists,[167] so there is little point in revisiting them here. However, it is worth concluding with a description of some of the issues and initiatives from around the world that were either mentioned in the surveys or which have not attracted much publicity. We have added some other points arising from interviews for this publication and from the implications of our research. Clearly, there are different priorities in different parts of the world and different contexts for different media types (the net, TV, radio, print) and genres (news, features, long-format, drama, blogs and so on). But we end with a list of eight, admittedly heterogeneous, ideas which we hope nevertheless have some resonance across cultures and can help both to get climate science into the media and improve the coverage of it. They are of course only suggestions and ideas to debate and not a blueprint for a utopian future.

1. Making it relevant

The media often focus on a 'doom and gloom' narrative and depressing reports about climate change (which sells newspapers and attracts viewers but is often remote to everyday experience). It is a harder challenge to tell engaging narratives of ordinary people around the world adapting to, or mitigating, its present and future effects. More of the 'empirical' angle 'what are people experiencing and what are they doing about it?' could replace the ubiquitous

---

[167] Science Media Centre, 'Climate Science in the Media', Feb. 2010: http://rogerpielkejr.blogspot. com/2010/02/climate-science-in-media.html. *Nature* magazine published an editorial which in effect was a blueprint for climate scientists' engagement with the media in 'Climate of Suspicion', *Nature*, 463/269 (21 Jan. 2010). The National Academy of Sciences published a report on 'Informing an Effective Response to Climate Change' in July 2010, which included twelve tips on how to communicate the science. See http://dels.nas.edu/resources/static-assets/materials-based-on-reports/reports-in-brief/Informing_Report_Brief_final.pdf.

reporting of the 'adversarial' such as 'Is it happening or not? Are humans to blame? Will the disaster come or not?' Some of the money spent by editors on sending journalists to summits like Copenhagen could be redirected to more investigations of local vulnerabilities and impacts, particularly for journalists in developing countries, and more on what states, cities, communities and individuals are doing all round the world to switch to low-carbon living.[168] The focus could be less on international targets and negotiations between big government and big industry, and more about relating climate change to ordinary people's lives.

Some organisations are already doing this. For example, Vietnam's Forum for Environment Journalists and the Ministry of Culture and Communication have organised an extensive programme of training for journalists where they are actually taken to areas of the country vulnerable to climate change impacts. A similar priority was stressed by an Indian scientist who commented that journalists there

> need to be given first-hand experience of issues wherever possible. For example, it's better to take them to coastal areas to explain sea level rise and its impact rather than giving them press releases and pictures.

Vietnam is also one of the many countries where the Earth Journalism Network (EJN) is very active. The EJN concentrates on local reporting of climate change impacts and building up networks of environment journalists.[169]

2. More science reports

News journalists often point out that too many scientists do not understand that their main priority is not to educate for the public good, but to sell a newspaper or get a good audience. A large part of that latter imperative is driven by what is newsworthy or simply new. A leading broadcast journalist for example says that in the current context of robust questioning of climate science, he needs more regular, peer-reviewed reports as strong pegs for

---

[168] See the discussion on city-level initiatives in the USA at Michael J. Coren, 'Where the Action Is: Climate Goes Local; Cities, Local Governments Confront Global Challenge', Yale Forum on Climate Change and the Media, 14 Sept. 2010.

[169] See Lisa Palmer, 'Environmental Reporters Receiving Training, to Cover Climate Change in Developing World', Yale Forum on Climate Change and the Media, 8 July 2010. The British Council's Climate4Media Programme also works with media professionals, concentrating on China, India and Africa. Since 2007, some 1,600 Chinese journalists have been trained. According to the Council, its programme challenged the assumption that it was impossible to work with state-controlled media as agents of change and demonstrated the effectiveness of the Chinese media in communicating climate change issues. A specialist website (www.climatereporting.cn) has also been created. The Thomson Reuters Foundation website, AlertNet Climate (www.alertnet.org/climate) includes stories of adaptation and mitigation from around the developing world.

keeping mainstream climate science high on the editorial agenda.

Our survey also showed that virtually all journalists want more regular updated reports on the science. The IPCC's next full assessment report (the fifth), for example, is not due until 2013 or 2014. Many argue that it needs to avoid having such long gaps between its reports, and that short summary updates on specific topics would undoubtedly help. The August 2010 official review of the IPCC by the InterAcademy Council raised the possibility of making the assessment reports shorter and less comprehensive by focusing on key issues or examining only significant new developments – these shorter reports could either replace the comprehensive assessments or alternate with them. However, it remains to be seen whether the governments who set the frequency of the IPCC reports will accept such suggestions. If they don't, then a strong case can be made for individual governments or scientific bodies to issue more frequent reports, and communicate them in an engaging and innovative way.

3. New media and new ideas to engage

Many commentators in the US and UK speak of climate fatigue from journalists, editors and the public alike. But the research by RISJ journalist fellow Margot O'Neill came up with an array of different approaches in the UK for new ways of telling stories and engaging audiences, from the BBC's *Newsnight*'s irreverent Ethical Man reports to the use of new media for data collection and sharing, online experiments and frontline citizen journalism and video reporting.[170] More stories about alternative energy and new technology solutions are often cited as a good approach to take.[171]

As for scientists, a powerful case has been made by several commentators to do more counter-blogging or just use the web more. For example, science writer Ben Goldacre, who is very critical of mainstream coverage of science in general, says that in addition to mainstream journalism, scientists should communicate directly with the public through the internet.[172] It is time-consuming of course, but it can improve the quality and integrity of the debate, and reaches a much wider audience than letters to the editor.[173] The website RealClimate is often held up as a good example of climate scientists' effective presence on the net.

---

[170] The *Guardian*'s interactive carbon calculators are an example and can be found at www.guardian.co.uk/environment/carbonfootprints.
[171] Margot O'Neill, 'Climate Change Reporting'.
[172] Zoe Corbyn, 'Trial by Error', *Times Higher Education* (26 Aug. 2010).
[173] Oliver Heffernan, 'Copenhagen: Why the Media Matters', Climate Feedback, 13 March 2009: http://blogs.nature.com/climatefeedback/2009/03/copenhagen_why_the_media_matte.html.

4. Climate scientist training

It was one of the strong results from the surveys that, although journalists and climate scientists ranked it differently, both of them thought the other needed more training as a high priority. The Science Media Centre (SMC) in London, which acts a bridge between journalists and scientists in the UK, was mentioned several times by UK journalists in the survey as the best organisation to work with. The SMC carries out regular training sessions for climate scientists. There are similar centres existing in Australia and New Zealand and more to open soon in Canada, Japan and Denmark. Much can be learnt from their experience, but they need more resources.

Some of the journalists in the survey argued that the science community needed to be trained how to engage not just with elites but with the general public: there is a need for high-profile figures who use short, sparky answers and deliver messages with an honesty and integrity that the public doesn't expect from politicians. One wrote that 'every scientist should be obliged to explain their work to a classroom of restless teenagers before being allowed anywhere near a camera'. Another spoke of the need for a 'Stephen Hawking or David Attenborough of climate science' who could inform and excite the public.

5. University press officers

The journalists surveyed did not think more training for university press officers (rather than scientists) was a priority. However, our research clearly shows a link between having effective press officers (in the NGO sector) and getting a message across. A strong case can be made for having more dedicated climate science press officers at universities or other organisations working on climate science. They could be freed from the more general tasks of institutional reputation management but give priority to (i) ensuring new and significant climate science gets into the media, (ii) stepping in quickly to help with the relevant expertise when mainstream climate science is questioned and (iii) having a presence at large international meetings where climate science is being discussed or where it forms an essential background. There is a precedent for dedicated subject-based press officers at the SMC whereby the engineering community and the mental health community have funded such posts for these subject areas.[174]

6. US initiatives for journalists

A new experiment launched in 2010 called Climate Desk aims to inject

---

[174] The idea of university press officers is mainly based on the experience of the SMC in the UK.

new life into what it calls the 'lacklustre' coverage of climate issues in most media outlets by concentrating on the stories that 'flesh out the human, environmental, economic and political impacts of a changing climate'.[175] The participating organisations, *The Atlantic*, the Center for Investigative Reporting, Grist, Mother Hone, Slate, Wired and a PBS show *Need to Know* have a combined online audience of 25 million monthly unique visitors, 1.5 million print readers and 1.5 million TV viewers. The non-profit *Miller-McCune* magazine has also attracted praise. It includes climate change coverage in its topics where the aim is to 'focus on practical options for solving serious problems, particularly if the options are backed by quality policy research and researchers'.[176]

7. US initiative for scientists

A Ph.D. student at the University of California, Berkeley, called Stacy Jackson with support from the AGU set up a 24/7 helpline for journalists covering the Copenhagen summit.[177] Dozens of university climate scientists were on hand to answer emails from 27 media organisations, which fired 54 questions at the online team. The questions were restricted to climate change science, not policy issues.

8. Checking credentials

Professor Carlos Nobre of INPE in Brazil speaks highly of a new initiative to check the credentials of any scientists:

> *All the Science-Environment sections of major newspapers report often on climate change issues reported in high visibility publications such as Science, Nature, PNAS etc. The op-ed pages, on the contrary, always seek the opinion of 'deniers', which in Brazil are poorly qualified scientifically. We have a wonderful system to immediately assess the list of publications of anyone posing as a scientist or researcher. It is called C V Lattes (www.cnpq.br). When I read some of these op-ed pieces of unknown scientists, I immediately check on the scientific accomplishments on C V Lattes. Without exception, they do not have quality, peer reviewed publications on their track record.*

[175] Thomas Zellers, 'Will Collaborative Climate Coverage Work?', *The Observatory: Columbia Journalism Review* (19 April 2010).
[176] See Bruce Lieberman, 'Miller-McCune — Non-Profit Publisher ... "Intelligent and Compelling Journalism"', 29 July 2010, Yale Forum on Climate Change and the Media.
[177] Mark Schrope, 'AGU Exploring Scientists–Journalists Link Developed in Copenhagen to Meet Media Needs', Yale Forum on Climate Change and the Media, 30 March 2010.

And for scientists checking out journalists, Simon Lewis, an expert on the Amazon from the University of Leeds in the UK, who was badly treated by the *Sunday Times*, has advocated a 'one-stop shop' for scientists where they can go and check out the track record of individual journalists, including any evidence of problems with their reporting in the past. This could help them to decide how to deal with them.[178]

To conclude, it is worth stressing that this publication has not been about the best way of communicating science in order to change people's minds or behaviour. That is the role of campaigners, policy institutes or governments. Nor has it focused on the growing body of fascinating literature on how different types of information the media disseminate and the ways they frame climate change provoke different reactions in those who consume it.[179] Rather its main message has been that, at a time of pressing need for more public understanding of the science, reporting climate science remains a huge challenge demanding a reinvigorated debate about new, interesting and engaging ways to do it. The fact that the world's media spent vast amounts of money and time concentrating on the drama of climate change negotiations at Copenhagen and under-reporting the science is yet more proof of how difficult a challenge this is going to be.

The mainstream media's role in the future should of course include the reporting of international negotiations (although as we mentioned in the last chapter, there is strong evidence at least in the UK that Copenhagen was a turn-off). It should also present information based on journalists' best understanding of where there is scientific consensus and where there is not, so that the general public can draw their own conclusions. Climate scientists need to engage with the media and help journalists and the public to do that. They should not stay encamped behind academic walls.

The phenomenon of extreme climatic events around the world in 2010 suggests that reporting people's experience of the weather will become more pressing an issue. Separate data from the NOAA and NASA published in July 2010 found that the first half of the year was the warmest on record globally. Seventeen countries – including Pakistan which registered a record temperature of 53.5C – have experienced record-breaking high temperatures. As Peter Stott of the UK Met Office explained, 'the evidence is so clear the chance there's something we haven't thought of [that could be warming the

---

[178] Quoted in Corbyn, 'Trial by Error'.
[179] See e.g. Susanne Moser, 'Understanding and Engagement in Climate Science', in Maxwell T. Boykoff (ed.), *The Politics of Climate Change* (2010); S. C. Moser and L. Dilling (eds), *Creating a Climate for Change: Communicating Climate Change and Facilitating Social Change* (Cambridge: Cambridge University Press, 2007), esp. pp. 64–80; S. O'Neill and S. Nicholson-Cole, (2009) '"Fear won't do it": Promoting Positive Engagement with Climate Change through Visual and Iconic Representations', *Science Communication*, 30 (2009), 355–79.

climate the other than GHGs] seems to be getting smaller and smaller'.[180] The story is not going to go away, and nor is the urgency of a profound and continuous debate between climate scientists and the media about how best to report it. At the risk of repetition, the imperative for both of them remains 'to make the significant interesting'.

---

[180] Fiona Harvey, 'New Data Fuel Debate on Climate', *Financial Times* (29 July 2010).

Acronyms

AGU	American Geophysical Union (AGU)
AOSIS	Alliance of Small Island States
BRIC	Brazil, Russia, India and China
CCMP	Climate Change Media Partnership
COP	Conference of the Parties
CRU	Climatic Research Unit (at the University of East Anglia)
ECI	Environmental Change Institute (Oxford University)
EIG	Environmental Integrity Group
EJN	Earth Journalism Network
EPA	Environmental Protection Agency (USA)
GHGs	Greenhouse Gases
IAC	InterAcademy Council
IIED	International Institute for Environment and Development
INPE	National Institute for Space Research (Brazil)
IPCC	Intergovernmental Panel on Climate Change

LDCs	Least Developed Countries
LSE	London School of Economics
NASA	National Aeronautics and Space Administration
NOAA	National Oceanic and Atmospheric Administration (USA)
NGOs	Non-Governmental Organisations
OUCE	Oxford University Centre for the Environment
REDD	Reducing Emissions from Deforestation and Forest Degradation
RINGO	Research and Independent Non-Governmental Organisations
RISJ	Reuters Institute for the Study of Journalism
SMC	Science Media Centre (UK)
UEA	University of East Anglia
UNEP	United Nations Environment Programme
UNFCCC	United Nations Framework Convention on Climate Change
WMO	World Meteorological Organisation

Bibliography

Simon Billett, 'Dividing Climate Change: Global Warming in the Indian Mass Media', *Climatic Change*, 99/1–2 (March 2010), 1-16.

Tammy Boyce and Justin Lewis (eds.), *Climate Change and the Media* (New York: Peter Lang, 2009).

Max Boykoff, 'Indian Media Representations of Climate Change in a Threatened Journalistic Ecosystem', *Climatic Change*, 99 (2010), 17–25.

Maxwell T. Boykoff (ed.), *The Politics of Climate Change* (London and New York: Routledge, 2010).

Maxwell T. Boykoff and Jules M. Boykoff, 'Climate Change and Journalistic Norms: A Case-Study of US Mass-Media Coverage', *Geoforum*, 38 (2007), 1190-1204.

Paddy Coulter and Atle Midttun (eds.), 'Escaping Climate Change: Climate Change in the Media: North and South Perspectives', CERES, June 2009: www.ceres21.org/webcontrol/UploadedDocumnets/Ceres21%20 Escaping%20Climate%20Change.pdf.

Elisabeth Eide, Risto Kunelius and Ville Kumpu, 'Domesticating a Global Moment: Transnational Study on the Coverage of Bali and Copenhagen Climate Summits. A Report from the MediaClimate project', paper presented at the IAMCR, Braga, July 2010.

Mike Hulme, *Why we Disagree about Climate Change* (Cambridge: Cambridge University Press, 2009).

Fred Pearce, *The Climate Files: The Battle for the Truth about Global Warming* (London: Guardian Books, 2010).

Science Media Centre, *Climate Science in the Media* (London: Science Media Centre, Feb. 2010).

David Shukman, *Reporting Live from the End of the World* (London: Profile Books, 2010).

RISJ Papers available via the RISJ website:

Cherelle Jackson, 'Staying afloat in Paradise: Reporting climate change in the Pacific', Hilary term 2010: http://reutersinstitute.politics.ox.ac.uk/fileadmin/documents/Publications/fellows__papers/2009-2010/Staying_afloat_in_Paradise.pdf.

Evelyn Tagbo, 'Media Coverage of Climate Change in Africa: A Case Study of Nigeria and South Africa', RISJ journalist fellowship paper, Hilary and Trinity terms 2010, forthcoming.

Margot O'Neill, 'Climate Change Reporting: A Stormy Forecast', RISJ journalist fellowship paper, Trinity Term 2010, forthcoming.

Regular commentary on the media and climate change (mostly US):

The Observatory: Columbia Journalism Review, available at http://www.cjr.org

The Yale Forum on Climate Change and the Media, available at http://www.yaleclimatemediaforum.org

Andy Revkin, *Dot Earth*, available at http://dotearth.blogs.nytimes.com/.

Appendix 1: Trust in the News

Latin America is typical of how television and radio remain the dominant ways in which most people in developing countries get their news, particularly for age groups above 35.[181] TV household penetration is above 90%, and has reached virtual saturation point in some countries. Radio receivers are equally if not more prevalent. Over 30% of the population are internet users, but less than 10% are estimated to read newspapers regularly.

The dominance of television is true of many other developing countries. According to a 2007 study of the international TV coverage of the 2007 IPCC reports:[182]

> *figures for India suggest a TV audience of 450 million a day compared to 205 million readers of newspapers and 37 million Internet users. In South Africa, 79 per cent of the population has access to television, compared to 42 per cent reading newspapers regularly and 6 per cent with access to the Internet. 98 per cent of China's population watch TV weekly compared to 31 per cent listening to radio and 35 per cent accessing the internet.*

Moreover, there is evidence to suggest that national television is not just the most used but the most trusted source of news in most countries by some distance, when compared to newspapers, news websites, radio and blogs. A 2006 Globescan/BBC/Reuters poll of more than 10,000 adults in ten countries suggested that 82% of those surveyed trusted national television the most. Only

---

[181] James Painter, *The Boom in Counter-Hegemonic News Channels: A Case Study of Telesur* (Oxford: RISJ, Sept. 2008), p. 25: http://reutersinstitute.politics.ox.ac.uk/fileadmin/documents/James_Painter.pdf.
[182] James Painter, 'All Doom and Gloom? International TV Coverage of the April and May 2007 IPCC Reports', paper presented at RISJ/ECI conference, Oxford, June 2007, p. 26, available at www.eci.ox.ac.uk/ news/ events/070727-carbonundrum/painter. Some caution should be taken with these figures as internet access has continued to increase since 2007, in the case of India e.g. more than doubling to 81 million in 2009; also, the figures are for general media consumption patterns rather than for the use of the different media for news.

16% did not trust it.[183] This compared with 38% trusting news websites, the second least trusted behind internet blogs (only 25% trusted). A more recent survey by Synovate and Deutsche Welle in May 2010 suggests that a majority of the 13,000 people questioned in 18 countries rated TV as the best media source for climate change information, followed by websites.[184]

The limitations of concentrating on 'elite' newspapers rather than TV news bulletins can be illustrated by the contrasting reach of the two media. The 2007 study of the international coverage of the IPCC reports concentrated on TV coverage precisely because the number of TV viewers was considerably higher in the six countries included (Brazil, China, India, Mexico, Russia and South Africa) than the number of readers of newspapers or users of the internet. The content analysis of six prime-time news bulletins on highly watched TV channels showed that there was no coverage at all of two of the seminal 2007 IPCC Fourth Assessment Reports (WG-2 and WG-3) on the main evening news bulletin of the most watched TV channels in three of the countries studied (India, Mexico and Russia) on the nights the reports were published. Brazil (TV Globo) was the only country to cover both reports.[185]

The key point here is that the low amount of TV coverage of the IPCC reports was not normally replicated in the print media in these countries. Several English-language newspapers in India included discussion or reporting of the 'impact' report (WG-2), whilst South African print media also reported it fairly extensively. Mexican newspapers had some coverage, in contrast to the silence of the main TV channel, Televisa.[186] But the audience reach is very different: the combined audience for the three news programmes not covering the reports at all was over 100 million.

In contrast, one of Mexico's leading newspapers, *Reforma*, covered the impact report, but has a circulation of less than 300,000. Likewise, the *Times of India* covered the report, but its readership, though extensive, is restricted to English speakers whereas *Aaj Tak* reaches an audience in Hindi, the official language of India spoken by more than 400 million people. Moreover, illiteracy rates are high in India, particularly amongst women.[187] Russian newspapers rarely cover climate change issues, but their reach is far less than national television from which 80% of Russians take their news – the next highest is national radio with 21%.

---

[183] This was true of all ten countries except Brazil where national or regional newspapers were the most trusted. BBC/Reuters/Media Center Poll; Trust in the Media, available at: www.globescan.com/news_archives/bbcreut.html.

[184] 'Climate Change Concern Remains High across the Globe, Says Synovate and Deutsche Welle Global Study', 28 May 2010: www.synovate.com/news/article/2010/05/climate-change-concern-remains-high-across-the-globe-says-synovate-and-deutsche-welle-global-study.html.

[185] Eight international TV channels monitored also offered greater coverage of the reports.

[186] Painter, 'All Doom and Gloom?', p. 10.

[187] Adult (15+ years) literacy rates in 2009 in India were 76.9% for men and 54.5% for women, according to the UN Population Fund's State of the World Population 2009.

Appendix 2: Attendees at Copenhagen

Methodology

The UNFCCC helpfully provides on their websites lists of the people who attend COP summits.[188] In the case of Copenhagen, there are participation statistics available for those who were pre-registered to attend and those who actually attended the summit. They are divided up into the three categories of parties (usually government delegates), observer organisations (mostly NGOs) and media. In the case of journalists, however, a breakdown of the 3,221 who were officially there at Copenhagen was not available, so we had to work from the list of pre-registered journalists.

Journalists

The UNFCCC media registration lists are divided into seven categories: news agency, daily, periodical, online, TV, radio and photo. They are listed by name of the journalist, followed by the media organisation the journalist works for. However, no details are given of the country of origin, so we used internet searches and other methods to assign each individual name to a country.

We kept as a separate category the journalist entries for 14 of the main international news agencies, namely Agence France-Presse (AFP), al Jazeera, Associated Press (AP), BBC, Bloomberg, CNN, Dow Jones, Getty, Google, Inter Press Service (IPS), International Herald Tribune, Reuters, United Press International (UPI) and 'other'. This was because it was not clear in many cases where the individual journalists working for the agencies were from, and also because the main target audience of these agencies was an international one. However, journalists from CBS were assigned to the USA, EFE to Spain, RFI

[188] Available via http://unfccc.int/documentation/documents/items/3595.php.

to France and Deutsche Welle to Germany, largely because the majority of the names seemed to suggest that the journalists came from those countries. In contrast, Reuters for example employs journalists from around 80 countries, whilst the entries for the BBC included several non-British journalists who work for the World Service which broadcasts or has internet sites in around 30 languages.

We also separated out from the country lists those journalists who were registered as working for regional bodies such as Euronews, CNBC Europe or Canal Africa as it was difficult to assign them to individual countries. In the case of two organisations, the Earth Journalism Network (EJN) and Internews, whose journalists were variously entered under news agency, TV or online, we consulted the CCMP website and EJN associate organisations to allocate the individual journalists (of whom there were around 37 at Copenhagen) to their countries of origin. The justification for doing this lay in the desire to get an accurate picture as possible about the presence of journalists from developing countries.

It is worth asking how much the separate categorisation of journalists from international agencies and regional bodies distorted the results. Of the 3,877 journalists pre-registered for Copenhagen, 3,487 were from individual countries, 336 were from the 14 international agencies and 54 came from regional bodies. The last two came to a total of 390, equivalent to about 10% of the total number of journalists registered. If the 390 journalists had been allocated to individual countries, it would have undoubtedly increased the numbers registered under the UK, the USA and other developed countries. The UK for instance would have had a significantly higher number.[189] But as the last two columns in Tables 2, 3, 5 and 7 show, this did not make a huge difference to the overall percentage figures when divided by regions and negotiating group.

The first column of Table 1 shows the 119 countries represented by a media presence at Copenhagen. The final column (6) shows the division between them of the 3,487 journalists who were pre-registered for the summit (11 were not able to be allocated). The columns in-between show to which region, subregion and negotiating bloc we assigned each country (for example, Turkey or Russia were assigned to Europe even though they could have been put in Asia).

Table 2 shows the total number of journalists broken down by regions. Column 1 shows the five regions they were from (AME = Africa and the Middle East; Asia-Pac = Asia-Pacific; Europe; Latam = Latin America; and

---

[189] It would have been difficult to disaggregate which of the 68 BBC employees pre-registered were working for BBC World News, BBC World Service or the language sites of the BBC, as against the various domestic BBC outlets. The BBC had the highest number registered of the international agencies, followed by Reuters and AP (both with 55).

USA/Can = USA and Canada). Of the 36 countries in the AME group, 29 were from Africa and 7 from the Middle East. Column 2 shows the number of countries represented from each region, column 3 the number of journalists from each of the five regions, and column 4 the average number of journalists per country in the region.

Column 5 shows the percentage of all journalists assigned to individual countries broken down by region, whilst columns 6 to 8 show the results when the regions are broken down into smaller regional or individual units. Finally, column 9 shows the percentage of journalists by region and subregion when all the journalists pre-registered are included (i.e. including the 390 journalists assigned to international agencies and regional bodies).

Table 3 shows the journalists broken down by negotiating bloc at the Copenhagen summit. Column 1 includes the G-77 plus China, of which there are around 130 member countries. LDCs (Least Developed Countries) and AOSIS (Alliance of Small Island States) countries are a subset of the G-77; there are 49 LDCs officially classified by the UN,[190] and most are to be found in Sub-Saharan Africa and Asia, whilst there are 39 member states and 4 observer states belonging to AOSIS.[191] A country can be an LDC and a member of AOSIS. The nine members of the Umbrella Group at the time of Copenhagen were all represented (USA, Japan, Norway, Australia, Canada, Russia, New Zealand, Ukraine and Iceland). Twenty-six of the 27 member states of the EU were also represented (the exception was Slovakia). The EIG stands for Environmental Integrity Group and at the time of Copenhagen had three members (Mexico, South Korea and Switzerland). Finally, 'others' includes countries who were not affiliated or whose affiliation was not known (e.g. some countries of the former Soviet Union like Belarus).

Column 3 shows the number of countries represented from each negotiating bloc, column 4 the number of journalists, column 5 the percentage of all journalists assigned to individual countries, and column 6 the percentage of all the journalists pre-registered.

We also examined the country of origin of the journalists at the previous two COP meetings in Bali (COP-13 in December 2007) and Poznan (COP-14 in December 2008). Unlike the Copenhagen summit, the list of journalists who were actually present at those two summits rather than those who were just pre-registered are available. These were divided into the same seven media categories as for Copenhagen. We separated out again the journalists from international agencies (the same list but without Google, IPS, UPI, and 'other', giving a total of ten) and the journalists from regional bodies. For Bali, this gave us a total of 1,498 journalists of which 1,317 were allocated to individual

---

[190] The official UN list of LDCs can be found here: www.unohrlls.org/en/ldc/related/62/.
[191] The list of AOSIS states can be found at www.sidsnet.org/aosis/members.html.

countries, 159 to agencies and 22 to regional bodies.

Table 4 shows the breakdown for the 1,317 journalists at Bali allocated to the 67 countries they were from. The columns are the same as in Table 1.

Table 5 shows the same breakdowns for Bali as shown for Copenhagen in Table 2. Figures for G-77 and LDC countries are included at the bottom of the table. Two rows are included, the first including Indonesia and the second not. We did not break down the figures fully by negotiating blocs, as these were different at Bali and Poznan compared to Copenhagen.

A total of 823 journalists were at Poznan from 65 countries, of which 750 were allocated to individual countries, 62 to agencies (AFP, AP, BBC, Bloomberg, Dow Jones, RTR, UPI and other), and 11 to regional bodies. Table 6 shows the breakdown for the 750 journalists, allocated to the 65 countries they were from. Again the columns are the same as in Table 1. Table 7 shows the same breakdowns for Poznan as Tables 2 and 5 do for Copenhagen and Bali.

Finally, we wanted to plot the historical trends from Poznan to Copenhagen. Figure A1 shows the number of journalists broken down by the five regions at the three summits, whilst Figure A2 breaks them down by percentages. Figure A3 does the same thing but this time only for G-77 and LDC countries. The figures for Indonesia are not included in the Bali figures. If they were, the G-77 representation would be much higher at 645, representing 43% of all journalists there.

We included the category of 'others' (i.e. journalists assigned to international agencies and regional bodies) in Figures A2 and A3 as it gave a more accurate picture of the percentage breakdowns. It is interesting to note that their percentage representation was pretty consistent across the three summits at 12 (Bali), 9 (Poznan) and 10 (Copenhagen).

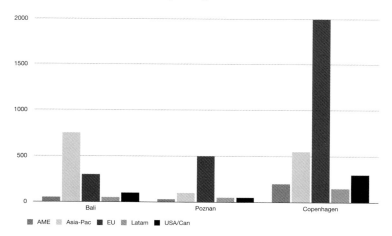

Figure A1. Trends in regional representation (numbers)

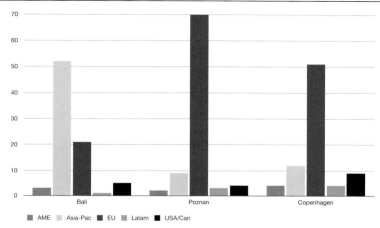

Figure A2. Trends in regional representation (%)

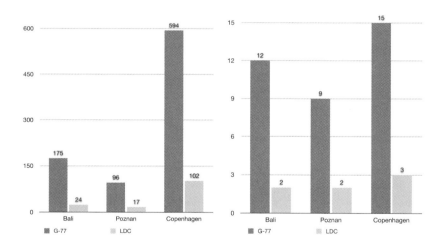

Figure A3. Trends in G-77 and LDC representation

There are some caveats to the figures found in the tables. For example, some people present at Copenhagen may have been registered as journalists, but could have been something else. Bjorn Lomborg, for instance, a well-known Danish commentator, author and sceptic on some aspects of climate change, was registered as a CNN journalist. Likewise, some journalists appeared under other UNFCCC registration categories. For example, five Bangladeshi journalists seem to have been registered under a Bangladeshi research centre, and fifteen appeared in the list of government representatives.

Universities and NGOs

Some of the universities belong to a network of research centres and organisations called RINGOs, which stands for Research and Independent Non-Governmental Organisations (to the UNFCCC). Their official aim is to 'develop sound strategies to address both the causes and consequences of global climate change'.[192] They contribute to UNFCCC meetings in a similar fashion to ENGOs (environment), BINGOs (business and industry), TUNGOs (trade unions) and LGMAs (local governments and municipal authorities). They hold regular meetings at the COP meetings.

Universities appear in the official UNFCCC participation lists under the category of NGOs, but do not appear as a separate category within it. Most of the participants attached to a university appeared under the heading of a university such as Ateneo de Manila University, Australian National University and so on. Working from the actual list of attendees (not those pre-registered),[193] we drew up a list of those universities and counted the number of people registered under each of them. The results can be seen in Table 8. The 88 universities listed in the table include Dartmouth College, Imperial College, the London School of Economics and the Massachusetts Institute of Technology (MIT) in Boston due to their reputational status. The table also includes the United Nations University even though it does not have a student body and is more like a research centre. A total of 1,677 people were registered to these 88 universities.

Several other attendees at Copenhagen are registered as being attached to a university but appear under a different heading either in the UNFCCC category of NGOs or under Parties, UN bodies, Specialised agencies and related organisations, and Intergovernmental organisations. We therefore did a word search entering 'university', 'université', 'universitat', and 'universidad(e)' to be able to include them in the total numbers of academics present. Using this method, we arrived at a total of 302 people registered under individual universities which had not been entered under the heading of a university.[194] Several of them appeared in the lists of government delegations, UN bodies and NGOs which were not universities.

The 302 people came from 189 universities, but of those 189 universities, 33 already appeared on the list of universities in Table 8. So the total number of universities with a presence of at least one representative was 88 plus 156 (i.e.

---

[192] See their official website at www.ringos.net/.
[193] The three pdfs can be found at: http://unfccc.int/resource/docs/2009/cop15/eng/inf01p01.pdf; http://unfccc.int/resource/docs/2009/cop15/eng/inf01p02.pdf; http://unfccc.int/resource/docs/2009/cop15/eng/inf01p03.pdf.
[194] There were some people registered under a different heading even though they were from the same university that had its own heading. E.g. Professor Yadvinder Mahli from the ECI at Oxford University was registered under the Gabon delegation.

189 less 33), which comes to a total of 244.

We then included a list of six other colleges on the assumption that the representatives were likely to be academics. These are listed in Table 9. We also selected a few academic associations or committees of scientists such as the American Geophysical Union in the USA and the Royal Society in the UK. The justification for their inclusion was that many of those listed were academics from universities not listed elsewhere.

Finally, we highlighted a few eminent research centres and institutes to get a flavour of how many people attended from such bodies as they were likely to be a good representation of scientists from, or linked to, academic institutions. The Potsdam Institute, the Woods Hole Research Center, the Wuppertal Institute and the John Heinz III Center for example are very well-known centres of excellence. We also wanted to include some non-Western centres such as the Bangladesh Centre for Advanced Studies, the Centre for Environment and Development in India and the Centre for Climate Change and Environmental Studies in Nigeria. Finally, meteorological institutes were included in the list as they are heavily populated with climate scientists, often with strong links to the academic world.

However, we did *not* count the vast numbers of representatives of institutes dealing with climate change and development (such as the Institute of Development Studies, Sussex University, and IIED in the UK), forestry and the Amazon, foundations, law schools, policy institutes, and energy or transport research centres. Nor did we include UN organisations such as UNEP, the WMO and the IPCC, even though many eminent scientists were entered under them.[195] However, individuals whose listings under the institutes, research centres or UN bodies included mention of the universities they were attached to would have made it onto the list above of the 302 not listed under the heading of universities.

Table 9 gives a total of 490 representatives from colleges, academic associations/committees and some research centres.

Finally we entered 'professor' as a word search into all the lists of attendees, and came up with a total of 280. They included the categories of assistant professor, acting professor, adjunct professor, associate professor, professor emeritus, junior professor and visiting professor.

It is important to stress that there are a number of limitations to these statistics. First, we do not know the area of expertise of those listings. Many could have been social scientists who had little to say about the natural sciences. Nor can we be sure of the status of all those listed under universities. Some of the best represented universities were either situated physically close to Copenhagen (the top three were Lund University, Technical University

---

[195] Numbers of attendees listed under UNEP were 81, WMO/UNEP-IPCC 25, and the WMO on its own 18.

of Denmark and University of Copenhagen) or included many students in their numbers. For example, the figure of 61 for Yale University includes more than 50 from the Yale Student Environment Coalition. Likewise, most of the 85 listed under Oxford University come from the Environmental Change Institute, and – like Yale – many were students.

To try and get a better sense of what percentage of those listed under universities were more experienced academics, we asked a representative of six universities how many of their delegations were senior scientists/ researchers (including professors) who published in peer-reviewed journals (as opposed to students).[196] The following results came back, based mostly on best estimates:

- University of Colorado at Boulder: 8 out of 12 (75%)

- Columbia University: 5 out of 7 (71%)

- London School of Economics (LSE): 17 out of 112 (15%)

- Lund University: 40 out of 230 (17%)

- Oxford University (ECI): 9 out of 85 (11%)

- Yale University: 10 out of 75 (13%)

Obviously, it is difficult to draw too many conclusions from a small sample. But for those universities with significant numbers of representatives at Copenhagen, like the LSE, the ECI, Yale and Lund, roughly between 10 and 20% would probably fit the category of experienced scientists. For those universities with lower numbers present (Colorado and Columbia), the figure rises steeply to over 70%. The higher percentage of researchers from these last two universities may be due in part to the higher travel costs limiting student participation.

It was beyond the scope of this paper to examine all those scientists who were attached to research centres not included in Table 9.[197] As noted above, we did not include the large numbers of such centres working on climate change and adaptation, mitigation, forestry and so on. The number of academic scientists at Copenhagen involved in research worthy of being quoted by the media

[196] Personal communications with author. In some cases, the respondents were working from the pre-registered figures rather than the actual attendees.
[197] Just to give one example of the limitations of our methodology: Carlos Nobre is from Brazil's National Institute for Space Research. He is one of Brazil's most respected scientists working on the Amazon and climate science, and a lead author for the IPCC. He was registered under the Brazilian government delegation so he would not have appeared in any of our lists of academic scientists.

would undoubtedly have been significantly higher than the figure of 500 we arrived at by sticking just to universities.

Communications officers

We wanted to get an idea of how many of the various organisations had media or communications people present within their delegations. For this, we entered the search words 'press', 'communications', 'information', 'media', and 'news'. We included those registered under 'press': officer, 'communications: officer, head, director, manager, coordinator, and online' (but not professor of), 'information: officer', 'media: director, officer, producer, interactive', and 'head of news'. We did not include photographers, video producers or editors (as 'editors' would have included publishing houses attached to universities).

Table 10 shows the universities listed in Table 8 which had people dealing with the media. The first column shows the numbers working in this capacity. As a point of comparison, we did the same exercise with the list of organisations in Table 9, and added three UN organisations listed as separate categories (UNEP, WMO/UNEP-IPCC and WMO) and three NGOs (Greenpeace, Oxfam and WWF). The results can be seen in Table 10. The Oxfam figure of six includes two Oxfam media officers listed under government delegations.

One caveat is that it may have been the case that some or many of those entered on the UNFCCC lists were involved in media operations but not listed as such. But if we apply the same criteria across all organisations, it is clear that NGOs like Greenpeace, Oxfam and WWF have the highest numbers of communication officers both in absolute terms and measured by the percentage of their overall delegation.

The figures for media officials working with official delegations mentioned in Chapter 3 were reached by a search of the words 'press', 'communication' and 'media' in the official UNFCCC list of parties.

Table 1 Number of journalists by country at Copenhagen

Country	Region	Subregion	Negotiating group	Subgroup	Total no. of journalists
Denmark	Europe	Europe/host nation	EU		507
USA	USA/Canada	USA	Umbrella Group		330
Germany	Europe	Europe	EU		266
France	Europe	Europe	EU		245
Japan	Asia-Pac	Japan	Umbrella Group		239
UK	Europe	Europe	EU		213
Sweden	Europe	Europe	EU		184
China	Asia-Pac	China	G-77		103
Norway	Europe	Europe	Umbrella Group		102
Brazil	Latin America	Brazil	G-77		100
Italy	Europe	Europe	EU		98
Spain	Europe	Europe	EU		97
Netherlands	Europe	Europe	EU		61
Belgium	Europe	Europe	EU		57
Australia	Asia-Pac	Aus/NZ	Umbrella Group		56
Canada	USA/Canada	Canada	Umbrella Group		52
Finland	Europe	Europe	EU		52
Switzerland	Europe	Europe	EIG		47
India	Asia-Pac	India	G-77		43
Bangladesh	Asia-Pac	Asia-Pac rest	G-77	LDC	38
Russia	Europe	Ex-SU	Umbrella Group		36
South Korea	Asia-Pac	Asia-Pac rest	EIG		27
Egypt	AME	Africa	G-77		25
Mexico	Latin America	Latam rest	EIG		23
Portugal	Europe	Europe	EU		22
Nepal	Asia-Pac	Asia-Pac rest	G-77	LDC	17
Austria	Europe	Europe	EU		16
Indonesia	Asia-Pac	Asia-Pac rest	G-77		16
Turkey	Europe	Europe	Not affiliated		15
Poland	Europe	Ex-SU	EU		15
Nigeria	AME	Africa	G-77		14
Philippines	Asia-Pac	Asia-Pac rest	G-77		14
South Africa	AME	Africa	G-77		14
Iran	AME	M East	G-77		13
Kenya	AME	Africa	G-77		13
Greece	Europe	Europe	EU		12
Venezuela	Latin America	Latam rest	G-77		11
Ireland	Europe	Europe	EU		10
Lebanon	AME	M East	G-77		10
New Zealand	Asia-Pac	Aus/NZ	Umbrella Group		9
Croatia	Europe	Ex-SU	Not affiliated		9
Singapore	Asia-Pac	Asia-Pac rest	G-77	AOSIS	9
Ukraine	Europe	Ex-SU	Umbrella Group		9
Czech Republic	Europe	Ex-SU	EU		8
Thailand	Asia-Pac	Asia-Pac rest	G-77		8
Argentina	Latin America	Latam rest	G-77		7
Cameroon	AME	Africa	G-77		7
UAE	AME	M East	G-77		7
Costa Rica	Latin America	Latam rest	G-77		6
Hungary	Europe	Ex-SU	EU		6
Malaysia	Asia-Pac	Asia-Pac rest	G-77		6
Pakistan	Asia-Pac	Asia-Pac rest	G-77		6
Tanzania	AME	Africa	G-77	LDC	6
Romania	Europe	Ex-SU	EU		6

Country	Region	Subregion	Negotiating group	Subgroup	Total no. of journalists
Estonia	Europe	Ex-SU	EU		5
Ethiopia	AME	Africa	G-77	LDC	5
Ghana	AME	Africa	G-77		5
Greenland	Europe	Europe	Not affiliated		5
Morocco	AME	Africa	G-77		5
Suriname	Latin America	Latam rest	G-77	AOSIS	5
Uganda	AME	Africa	G-77	LDC	5
Albania	Europe	Ex-SU	Not affiliated		4
Algeria	AME	Africa	G-77		4
Bulgaria	Europe	Ex-SU	EU		4
Colombia	Latin America	Latam rest	G-77		4
DR Congo	AME	Africa	G-77	LDC	4
Macedonia	Europe	Ex-SU	Not affiliated		4
Peru	Latin America	Latam rest	G-77		4
Serbia	Europe	Ex-SU	Not affiliated		4
Sierra L	AME	Africa	G-77	LDC	4
Slovenia	Europe	Ex-SU	EU		4
Vietnam	Asia-Pac	Asia-Pac rest	G-77		4
Zambia	AME	Africa	G-77	LDC	4
Bhutan	Asia-Pac	Asia-Pac rest	G-77	LDC	3
Jordan	AME	M East	G-77		3
Latvia	Europe	Ex-SU	EU		3
Luxembourg	Europe	Europe	EU		3
Malta	Europe	Europe	EU		3
Papua New G	Asia-Pac	Asia-Pac rest	G-77	AOSIS	3
Bolivia	Latin America	Latam rest	G-77		2
Cape Verde	AME	Africa	G-77	AOSIS	2
Cyprus	Europe	Europe	EU		2
Ecuador	Latin America	latam rest	G-77		2
Eritrea	AME	Africa	G-77	LDC	2
Guyana	Latin America	Latam rest	G-77	AOSIS	2
Israel	AME	M East	Not affiliated		2
Iceland	Europe	Europe	Umbrella Group		2
Kuwait	AME	M East	G-77		2
Madagascar	AME	Africa	G-77	LDC	2
Mauritius	AME	Africa	G-77	AOSIS	2
Mongolia	Asia-Pac	Asia-Pac rest	Not affiliated		2
Syria	AME	M East	G-77		2
Afghanistan	Asia-Pac	Asia-Pac rest	G-77	LDC	1
Belarus	Europe	Ex-SU	Not affiliated		1
Benin	AME	Africa	G-77	LDC	1
Botswana	AME	Africa	G-77		1
Burkina Faso	AME	Africa	G-77	LDC	1
Chile	Latin America	Latam rest	G-77		1
Cuba	Latin America	Latam rest	G-77	AOSIS	1
El Salvador	Latin America	Latam rest	G-77		1
Faroe Islands	Europe	Europe	Not known		1
Guatemala	Latin America	Latam rest	G-77		1
Haiti	Latin America	Latam rest	G-77	AOSIS/LDC	1
Ivory Coast	AME	Africa	G-77		1
Jamaica	Latin America	Latam rest	G-77	AOSIS	1
Lithuania	Europe	Ex-SU	EU		1
Mali	AME	Africa	G-77	LDC	1
Marshall Islands	Asia-Pac	Asia-Pac rest	G-77	AOSIS	1
Mauritania	AME	Africa	G-77	LDC	1
Monte Carlo	Europe	Europe	Not known		1

Country	Region	Subregion	Negotiating group	Subgroup	Total no. of journalists
Montenegro	Europe	Ex-SU	Not affiliated		1
Mozambique	AME	Africa	G-77	LDC	1
Rwanda	AME	Africa	G-77	LDC	1
Samoa	Asia-Pac	Asia-Pac rest	G-77	AOSIS/LDC	1
Senegal	AME	Africa	G-77	LDC	1
Sri Lanka	Asia-Pac	Asia-Pac rest	G-77		1
Sudan	AME	Africa	G-77	LDC	1
Tajikistan	Asia-Pac	Asia-Pac rest	Not affiliated		1
Togo	AME	Africa	G-77	LDC	1
					3,476
Unknown					11
			Total no. of journalists		3,487

Table 2 Journalists by region (Copenhagen)

Region	No. of countries represented	No. of journalists	Average no. of journalists per country	% of all journalists assigned to individual countries	By subregion	No. of journalists	% of all journalists assigned to individual countries	% of all journalists registered
AME	36	173	5	5				
					Africa	134	4	3
					Middle East	39	1	1
Asia-Pac	23	608	26	17				
					Australia	56	2	1
					China	103	3	3
					Japan	239	7	6
					Rest of Asia-Pac	210	6	5
Europe	41	2,141	52	61				
					Denmark	507	15	13
					Germany	266	8	7
					France	245	8	6
					UK	213	6	5
					Rest of Europe	910	26	23
Latam	17	172	10	5				
					Brazil	100	3	3
					Rest of Latin America	72	2	2
USA/Can	2	382	191	11				
					USA	330	9	9
					Canada	52	1	1
Unknown		11		0		11	0	0
Other (agencies and regions)								10
Totals	119	3,487		100		3,487	100	100

Table 3 Journalists by negotiating bloc (Copenhagen)

Negotiating bloc		No. of countries	No. of journalists	% of all journalists assigned to individual countries	% of all journalists registered
G-77		68	594	17	15
Of which	LDC	23	102	3	3
	AOSIS	11	25	1	1
Umbrella Group		9	835	24	21
EU		26	1,900	54	49
EIG		3	97	3	3
Others		13	61	2	2
Agencies/regionals					10
Totals		119	3,487	100	100

Table 4 Number of journalists by country at Bali

Country	Region	Subregion	Negotiating group	Subgroup	Total no. of journalists
Indonesia	Asia-Pac	Asia-Pac/host nation	G-77		470
Japan	Asia-Pac	Japan			131
USA	USA/Canada	USA			81
Australia	Asia-Pac	Aus/NZ			72
UK	Europe	Europe			69
Germany	Europe	Europe			62
China	Asia-Pac	China	G-77		32
France	Europe	Europe			31
Spain	Europe	Europe			30
Denmark	Europe	Europe			29
Norway	Europe	Europe			23
Switzerland	Europe	Europe			21
Singapore	Asia-Pac	Asia-Pac	G-77		19
Thailand	Asia-Pac	Asia-Pac	G-77		19
Canada	USA/Canada	Canada			16
Netherlands	Europe	Europe			16
South Korea	Asia-Pac	Asia-Pac			16
Sweden	Europe	Europe			15
Brazil	Latin America	Brazil	G-77		14
India	Asia-Pac	India	G-77		13
Italy	Europe	Europe			13
Bangladesh	Asia-Pac	Asia-Pac	G-77	LDC	10
Belgium	Europe	Europe			10
Austria	Europe	Europe			9
Malaysia	Asia-Pac	Asia-Pac	G-77		9

Country	Region	Subregion	Negotiating group	Subgroup	Total no. of journalists
Finland	Europe	Europe			5
South Africa	AME	Africa	G-77		5
Sri Lanka	Asia-Pac	Asia-Pac	G-77		5
Egypt	AME	M East/Afr	G-77		4
Ireland	Europe	Europe			4
Portugal	Europe	Europe			4
Vietnam	Asia-Pac	Asia-Pac	G-77		4
Greece	Europe	Europe			3
Iran	AME	M East	G-77		3
Kenya	AME	Africa	G-77		3
Mexico	Latin America	Latam rest			3
Nepal	Asia-Pac	Asia-Pac	G-77	LDC	3
Czech Republic	Europe	Europe			2
DRC	AME	Africa	G-77	LDC	2
Israel	AME	M East			2
Kuwait	AME	M East	G-77		2
Mongolia	Asia-Pac	Asia-Pac	G-77		2
Nigeria	AME	Africa	G-77		2
Pakistan	Asia-Pac	Asia-Pac	G-77		2
Palau	Asia-Pac	Asia-Pac	G-77		2
Russia	Europe	Ex-SU			2
Uganda	AME	Africa	G-77	LDC	2
Bhutan	Asia-Pac	Asia-Pac	G-77	LDC	1
Botswana	AME	Asia-Pac	G-77		1
Burma (Myanmar)	Asia-Pac	Asia-Pac	G-77	LDC	1
El Salvador	Latin America	Latam rest	G-77		1
Haiti	Latin America	Latam rest	G-77	LDC	1
Jamaica	Latin America	Latam rest	G-77		1
Kazakhstan	Asia-Pac	Ex-SU	Not affiliated		1
Laos	Asia-Pac	Asia-Pac	G-77	LDC	1
Morocco	AME	Africa	G-77		1
Namibia	AME	Africa	G-77		1
New Zealand	Asia-Pac	Aus/NZ			1
PNG	Asia-Pac	Asia-Pac	G-77		1
Poland	Europe	Ex-SU			1
Qatar	AME	M East	G-77		1
Rwanda	AME	Africa	G-77	LDC	1
Samoa	Asia-Pac	Asia-Pac	G-77	LDC	1
Sudan	AME	Africa	G-77	LDC	1
Suriname	Latin America	Latam rest	G-77		1
Taiwan	Asia-Pac	Asia-Pac	Not affiliated		1
Timor E	Asia-Pac	Asia-Pac	G-77	LDC	1
Zimbabwe	AME	Africa	G-77		1
		Total no. of journalists			1,317

Table 5 Journalists by region (Bali)

Region	No. of countries	No. of journalists registered by country	Average no. of journalists by country	% of all journalists	By subregion	No. of journalists	% of all journalists assigned to individual countries	% of all journalists registered
AME	16	32	2	2				
					Africa	24	2	2
					M East	8	1	1
Asia-Pac	24	818	34	62				
					Australia	72	6	5
					China	32	2	2
					Indonesia	470	36	31
					Japan	131	10	9
					Rest of Asia-Pac	113	9	7
Europe	19	349	18	27				
					Germany	62	5	4
					France	31	2	2
					UK	69	5	5
					Rest of Europe	187	14	12
Latam	6	21	4	2				
					Brazil	14	1	1
					Rest of Latam	7	1	0
USA/Can	2	97	49	7				
		1317			Canada	16	1	1
					USA	81	6	5
Other (agencies and regions)								12
Totals	67	1317		100		1317	100	100
G-77	39	645	17	49				43
G-77*	38	175	5	13				12
LDC	12	24	2	2				2

* Not including Indonesia

Table 6 Number of journalists by country at Poznan

Country	Region	Subregion	Negotiating group	Subgroup	No. of journalists
Poland	EU	EU/host nation			325
Germany	EU	Germany			49
Japan	Asia-Pac	Japan			41
UK	EU	UK			41
USA	USA/Canada	USA			27
Spain	EU	EU			25
France	EU	France			22
Denmark	EU	EU			20
Norway	EU	EU			19
Sweden	EU	EU			16
Netherlands	EU	EU			15
Switzerland	EU	EU			14
Italy	EU	EU			12
Brazil	Latam	Brazil	G-77		11
China	Asia-Pac	China	G-77		10
Belgium	EU	EU			9
Austria	EU	EU			7
Mexico	Latam	Latam rest			7
India	Asia-Pac	Asia-Pac	G-77		6
Australia	Asia-Pac	Aus/NZ			5
Canada	USA/Can	Canada			5
Greece	EU	EU			4
South Africa	AME	Africa	G-77		4
Bangladesh	Asia-Pac	Asia-Pac	G-77	LDC	3
Indonesia	Asia-Pac	Asia-Pac	G-77		3
Kenya	AME	Africa	G-77		3
Peru	Latam	Latam rest	G-77		3
South Korea	Asia-Pac	Asia-Pac			3
Czech Republic	EU	EU			2
Hungary	EU	EU			2
Malaysia	Asia-Pac	Asia-Pac	G-77		2
Philippines	Asia-Pac	Asia-Pac	G-77		2
Antigua	Latam	Latam rest	G-77		1
Argentina	Latam	Latam rest	G-77		1
Bhutan	Asia-Pac	Asia-Pac	G-77	LDC	1
Botswana	AME	Africa	G-77		1
Burma	Asia-Pac	Asia-Pac	G-77	LDC	1
Cambodia	Asia-Pac	Asia-Pac	G-77	LDC	1
Cameroon	AME	Africa	G-77		1
Colombia	Latam	Latam rest	G-77		1
DRC	AME	Africa	G-77	LDC	1
Ethiopia	AME	Africa	G-77	LDC	1
Fiji	Asia-Pac	Asia-Pac	G-77		1
Finland	EU	EU			1

Country	Region	Subregion	Negotiating group	Subgroup	No. of journalists
Ghana	AME	Africa	G-77		1
Haiti	Latam	Latam rest	G-77	LDC	1
Ireland	EU	EU			1
Jamaica	Latam	Latam rest	G-77		1
Laos	Asia-Pac	Asia-Pac	G-77	LDC	1
Liberia	AME	Africa	G-77	LDC	1
Madagascar	AME	Africa	G-77	LDC	1
Malawi	AME	Africa	G-77	LDC	1
Malta	EU	EU			1
Mongolia	Asia-Pac	Asia-Pac	G-77		1
Namibia	AME	Africa	G-77		1
Nigeria	AME	Africa	G-77		1
Portugal	EU	EU			1
Samoa	Asia-Pac	Asia-Pac	G-77	LDC	1
Senegal	AME	Africa	G-77	LDC	1
Sierra Leone	AME	Africa	G-77	LDC	1
Suriname	Latam	Latam rest	G-77		1
Thailand	Asia-Pac	Asia-Pac	G-77		1
Uganda	AME	Africa	G-77	LDC	1
UAE	AME	M East	G-77		1
Vietnam	Asia-Pac	Asia-Pac	G-77		1
		Total no. of journalists			750

Table 7 Journalists by region (Poznan)

Region	No. of Countries	No. of journalists registered by country	Average no. of journalists by country	% of all journalists	By subregion	No. of journalists	% of all journalists assigned to individual countries	% of all journalists registered
AME	16	21	1	3				
					Africa	20	3	2
					M East	1	0	0
Asia-Pac	18	84	5	11				
					Australia	5	1	1
					China	10	1	1
					Japan	41	5	5
					Rest of Asia-Pac	28	4	3
Europe	20	586	29	78				
					France	22	3	3
					Germany	49	7	6
					Poland	325	43	39
					UK	41	5	5

Region	No. of Countries	No. of journalists registered by country	Average no. of journalists by country	% of all journalists	By subregion	No. of journalists	% of all journalists assigned to individual countries	% of all journalists registered
					Rest of Europe	149	20	18
Latam	9	27	3	4				
					Brazil	11	1	1
					Rest of Latam	16	2	2
USA/Can	2	32	16	4				
					Canada	5	1	1
					USA	27	4	3
Other (Agencies and regions)								9
Totals	65	750		100		750	100	100
G-77	39	76	2	10				9
LDC	15	17	1	2				2

Table 8 Number of attendees at Copenhagen by university

Ateneo de Manila University	3		Imperial College, London	10	
Australian National University	52	10th	Korea University	8	
Boston University	7		Kyoto University	2	
Brahma Kumaris Spiritual University	16		London School of Economics	57	8th
Brown University - Watson Institute	4		Lund University	158	1st
Colorado State University	3		Macquarie University	2	
Columbia University	7		Marmara University	3	
Cornell University	12		Massachusetts Institute of Technology	7	
Dartmouth College, USA	7		Mie University	6	
DePaul University	20		Northeastern University	18	
Duke University	14		Norwegian University of Science and Technology	6	
Eberhard Karls Universitat Tubingen	22		Open University	13	
Erasmus University Rotterdam	6		Pennsylvania State University	2	
Freie Universität Berlin	2		Purdue University	2	
Free University Amsterdam	13		Pusan National University	5	
Friedrich Schiller University Jena	10		Ryerson University	1	
George Mason University	4		Stanford University	57	8th
Georgetown University	18		Technical University Munich	13	
HafenCity University Hamburg	5		Technical University of Denmark	100	2nd
Harvard University	4				

Technische Universität Darmstadt	1	
Tsinghua University, Global CC Institute	3	
Umea University	7	
United Nations University	37	
Universidad Politécnica de Cataluna	6	
Université Laval	1	
Université Libre de Bruxelles,	3	
University Corporation for Atmospheric research	5	
University Luigi Bocconi	3	
University of Amsterdam	1	
University of Bayreuth	23	
University of Calgary	11	
University of California	72	5th
University of Cambridge	19	
University of Cape Town	12	
University of Copenhagen	93	3rd
University of Colorado at Boulder	12	
University of Delaware	4	
University of East Anglia	15	
University of Edinburgh	50	
University of Freiburg	15	
University of Gothenburg	40	
University of Guelph	1	
University of Hamburg	68	6th
University of Heidelberg	47	
University of Hong Kong	14	

University of Iceland	24	
University of Linköping	28	
University of Melbourne	7	
University of Michigan	29	
University of New South Wales	8	
University of Nijmegen	23	
University of Oslo	1	
University of Oxford	85	4th
University of Potsdam	21	
University of Queensland	7	
University of Regina	5	
University of Stuttgart	2	
University of Sussex - Sussex Energy Group	4	
University of Tampere	23	
University of Technology, Sydney	2	
University of Tokyo	22	
University of Toronto	8	
University of Twente	19	
Victoria University Wellington	18	
Wayne State University	1	
Widener University	9	
Yale University	61	7th
York University	8	
TOTAL	**1,677**	

Table 9 Number of attendees by other academic categories

Colleges

College of the Atlantic	17
Dickinson College	17
Ithaca College New York	25
Lewis and Clark College	9
Moravian College	20
Pomona College	20
Total	108

Academic Associations

American Geophysical Union	3
Association of American Geographers	7
Association of Science technology centres	4
China Association for Science and Technology	7
International Council for Science	7
The Royal Society	3
Scientific Committee on Antarctic Research	1
Scientific Committee on Problems of the Environment	6
Union of Concerned Scientists	11
Total	49

Research Centres and Institutes

Bangladesh Centre for Advanced Studies	17
Carnegie Institution for Washington	5
Center for International Climate and Environmental Research	18
Centre for Climate Change and Environmental Studies	5
Centre for Environment and Development	24
Centre for Science and Environment	9
Danish Meteorological Institute	24
H. John Heinz III Center for Science, Economics and the Environment	7
IVL Swedish Environmental Research Institute Ltd.	13
Korea Institute of Science and Technology Europe	2
MET Office Hadley Centre	7
Oeko-Institut, e.V.	5
Potsdam Institute for Climate Impact Research	34
Research Centre Juelich	2
Royal Netherlands Meteorological Institute	8
Stockholm Environment Institute	61
The Woods Hole Research Center	35
Winrock International	4
Wuppertal Institute for Climate, Environment and Energy	10
Total	290

Table 10 Number of press or communication officers at Copenhagen

Universities

Australian National University	1
Georgetown University	1
Harvard University	1
Korea University	1
London School of Economics	1
Lund University	1
Open University	1
Technical University of Denmark	1
United Nations University	2
University of Copenhagen	1
University of East Anglia	1
Total	12

Research Centres and Institutes

Center for International Climate and Environmental Research	4
Danish Meteorological Institute	2
IVL Swedish Environmental Research Institute Ltd.	2
MET Office Hadley Centre	2
Royal Netherlands Meteorological Institute	1
Stockholm Environment Institute	2
The Woods Hole Research Center	1
Total	14

Academic Associations/Committees

International Council for Science	1
Union of Concerned Scientists	1
Total	2

UN Bodies

UNEP	4
WMO/UNEP-IPCC	1
WMO	2
Total	7

NGOs

Greenpeace	20
Oxfam	6
WWF	10
Total	36

Appendix 3: Details of Newspapers Included in Content Analysis

Australia

The *Sydney Morning Herald* is a broadsheet with an audience target of AB socio-economic class. It has a reach of 800,000 and a circulation of 210,000.

The *Daily Telegraph* is a tabloid with a demographic of blue- and white-collar workers. It has a reach of one million and a circulation of 360,000.

Brazil

Folha de S. Paulo, the biggest broadsheet in Brazil, sells 295,000 copies on average per day, across the country. It has a target audience of ABs.

Super Noticia, the most successful tabloid in Brazil, sells 300,000 copies per issue. It reaches as far as the south-eastern state of Minas Gerais. Its cover price is kept low.

China

People's Daily, an official party organ of the Chinese communist party, is the largest circulation daily newspaper in China, with 2.3 million in 2008. It mainly targets leaders at different levels and in different sectors of China. The general public seldom read it and its retail sales are low.

Beijing Evening News is a popular mainstream newspaper with official daily sales of more than one million copies, making it the most widely circulated of the evening newspapers. It combines hard and soft news in an accessible style.

Egypt

Al-Akhbar (The News) is a semi-official, state-owned daily newspaper; it is one of the three main state-owned dailies.

Al-Masri al-Youm (The Egyptian Today) is an independent daily newspaper. It began publishing in 2004 and is now one of the top selling newspapers in Egypt, rivalling *al-Ahram*, the government's flagship daily.

India

The *Times of India* is an English-language daily broadsheet aimed at higher income group readers. Its readership is more than 13 million, which is reputedly the largest circulation of any English-language newspaper globally.

Dainik Bhaksar is a mass-audience Hindi daily broadsheet with a readership of 31.9 million. Relative to the *Times of India*, its readership includes lower income groups.

Italy

Corriere della Sera is a broadsheet with the largest sales of any newspaper in the country (over 600,000 copies a day). It is aimed more at upper income groups, and is more rooted in northern and central parts of the country.

Il Giorno is closer to the UK tabloid model than most Italian papers. It has a distribution of around 70,000 copies.

Mexico

La Reforma has about 275,000 readers in Mexico City. However, it shares content with other papers in the parent newsgroup Grupo Reforma, which has a total readership of over 400,000. It is a paper of choice for the socio-economic elite.

Uno Más Uno is one of Mexico's most successful tabloids, with a lower income group audience profile.

Nigeria

The *Guardian* targets the middle and upper class (AB socio-economic class).

The *Sun* is the country's leading tabloid with a target audience of the middle and lower classes (BC). Its reach is right across the country, and its circulation is an average of 130,000 per day.

Russia

Kommersant is a business-oriented newspaper, with a circulation of 250,000. Its target audience is mainly men, often managers and professionals with a higher than average income.

Komsomolskaya Pravda is a tabloid newspaper, with a circulation of 800,000. It particularly targets women and pensioners.

UK

The *Guardian* is a broadsheet newspaper with a left-liberal political slant. In May 2010 it had a daily circulation of 300,000; 90% of its readers are from socio-economic groups ABC1.

The *Daily Mail* is a tabloid newspaper with a conservative, populist slant. In May 2010 it had a daily circulation of over 2 million, making it the second largest UK newspaper after the *Sun*. Its readership is spread across all classes.

USA

The *New York Times* has a circulation of 928,000 daily and 20 million web visitors per month in March 2009. It has a liberal slant and targets an AB audience.

The *New York Post* is a tabloid newspaper with a circulation of approximately 500,000 daily. It is owned by Rupert Murdoch's News Corporation, and is seen as being sensationalist and conservative.

Vietnam

VietnamNet is a Hanoi-based online news portal with a nearly 7 million unique users in Jan 2010.

Zing is a Ho Chi Minh-based entertainment online portal with a strong tabloid profile. It had 15 million unique users in January 2010.

Appendix 4: Text of Research Questionnaire for Content Analysis

Research Questionnaire, Copenhagen coverage

1. Name of researcher, country:

2. Which two examples of the print media did you monitor?

Please include any data you may have on their audience target, reach and circulation.

3. How many articles were published on each day?

December 7:   December 8:   December 9
December 18:   December 19:   December 20

4. Within the articles you monitored, what percentage (roughly) of the total article included mention or discussion of the science of climate change?

0–10%:   10–50%:   50–100%:

5. When the science was quoted, how many times were reports, books or studies from the following organisations mentioned?

IPCC or UNFCCC:

International bodies other than the IPCC/UNFCCC (like Red Cross, UNEP, UNDP, WMO, etc):

National organisations (like government bodies, UK Met Office, US EPA, etc):

NGOs (like Oxfam, Greenpeace, WWF, Friends of the Earth):

> Of which, national NGOs:
> International NGOs:

Named scientists/academics from universities or research institutes:

Individual scientists or experts where the academic affiliation is not mentioned:

Generic quoting of 'scientists' without naming individuals:

Sceptics: Companies or Businesses: Other:

6. When individuals (rather than reports) are quoted on the science of climate change, who got quoted and how many times?

National government officials or politicians:

Officials from the UNFCCC or IPCC:

Representatives of international bodies other than the UNFCCC or

IPCC:

NGO representatives:

> Of which national:
> International:

Scientists/academics from:

> Universities or research institutes:
> Government bodies:
> Think tanks, NGOs or other:
> Sceptics:
> Companies or Businesses:
> Other:

7. At the end of the conference (December 19 and 20), who got quoted on their reaction to the Political Accord signed by the USA, Brazil, China, India and South Africa?

> Government officials or politicians:
> Of which national:
> International:
> Officials from the UNFCCC or IPCC:
> Representatives of international bodies other than the UNFCCC or IPCC:
> NGO representatives:
> Of which national:
> International:
> Scientists/academics from:
> Universities or research institutes:
> Government bodies:
> Think tanks, NGOs or other:
> Sceptics:
> Companies or Businesses:
> Other:

8. Any other interesting points you would like to mention?

Appendix 5: Coverage of Copenhagen Summit in the Media in 12 Countries

Part 1

		Australia Sydney Morning / Sunday Herald	Australia Daily/Sunday Telegraph	Brazil Folha	Brazil Super Notícia	China People's Daily	China Beijing Evening News	Egypt Al-Akhbar	Egypt al-Masri al-Youm	India Times of India	India Dainik Bhaskar	Italy Corriere della Sera	Italy Il Giorno
Number of articles		24	16	86	2	16	20	1	2	52	24	24	13
Science %													
	<10%	16	11	73	1	15	14	1	2	39	21	19	10
	10–50%	2	0	8	1	1	3	0	0	11	3	2	2
	50–100%	6	5	5	0	0	3	0	0	2	0	3	1
Who gets quoted (reports)?													
IPCC/UNFCCC		2	4	5	1	2	1	0	0	2	2	0	1
Other int bodies		2	1	4	0	0	1	0	0	0	0	1	2
National organisations		1	0	5	0	2	1	0	0	3	0	1	1
NGOs		0	1	1	0	1	0	0	0	2	1	0	0
Scientists individual		0	1	0	0	0	0	0	0	4	0	0	0
Scientists generic		0	0	4	1	0	5	0	0	5	0	1	1
Sceptics		0	0	2*	0	0	0	0	0	1*	0	1	0
Who gets quoted (individuals)?													
IPCC/UNFCCC		3	0	4	0	0	0	0	0	2	2	1	1
Other int bodies		0	0	5	0	0	1	0	0	1	1	0	1
National organisations or politicians		1	0	2	0	2	6	0	0	6	3	6	1
NGOs		0	0	1	0	0	0	0	0	4	3	0	1
Scientists individual		5	0	4	0	4	0	0	0	2	0	0	0
Sceptics		0	0	0	0	0	0	0	0	1*	0	0	0
Other		0	0	0	0	0	0	0	0	1	0	0	0
Reactions to the Copenhagen Accord													
Government officials		11	11	26	0	0	12	6	10	26	6	2	5
IPCC/UNFCCC		0	0	2	0	0	0	0	0	0	0	0	1
Other int bodies		1	0	3	0	0	0	0	0	0	1	1	0
NGOs		1	2	6	0	0	0	0	2	1	0	2	1
Scientists		1	0	1	0	0	1	0	0	0	0	1	0
Sceptics		0	0	0	0	0	0	0	0	0	0	0	0
Other		0	0	0	0	0	0	0	0	2	0	0	0

* generic

Part 2

		Mexico La Reforma	Mexico Uno Más Uno	Nigeria Guardian	Nigeria Sun	Russia Kommersant	Russia Komsomolskaya pravda	UK The Guardian/Observer	UK Daily Mail/Mail on Sunday	USA New York Times	USA New York Post
Number of articles		22	5	12	1	10	2	34	5	19	11
Science %											
	<10%	15	5	7	1	9	2	25	4	14	8
	10–50%	4	0	4	0	1	0	4	1	2	3
	50–100%	3	0	1	0	0	0	5	0	3	0
Who gets quoted (reports)?											
IPCC/UNFCCC		3	0	4	0	4	0	1	0	2	0
Other int bodies		2	0	4	0	1	0	2	0	0	0
National organisations		3	0	4	0	0	0	2	1	4	0
NGOs		0	0	1	0	0	0	1	0	-0	0
Scientists individual		1	0	0	0	0	0	0	0	1	0
Scientists generic		1	0	1	0	0	0	1	1	0	1
Sceptics		0	0	1*	0	0	0	0	0	0	0
Other		0	0	0	0	0	0	0	0	0	0
Who gets quoted (individuals)?											
IPCC/UNFCCC		0	0	1	0	0	0	3	0	0	1
Other int bodies		1	0	1	0	0	0	5	0	1	1
National organisations or politicians		0	0	4	1	0	0	5	0	1	1
NGOs		0	0	1	0	0	0	7	0	0	0
Scientists individual		2	0	0	0	3	0	0	1	2	1
Sceptics		0	0	0	0	0	0	0	0	1	0
Other		0	0	0	0	0	0	0	0	0	0
Reactions to the Copenhagen Accord											
Government officials		6	2	4	0	1	0	24	3	4	4
IPCC/UNFCCC		0	0	1	0	0	0	2	0	3	0
Other int bodies		0	0	1	0	0	0	0	1	1	0
NGOs		2	0	4	0	0	0	15	3	1	4
Scientists		0	0	0	0	0	0	6	0	0	0
Sceptics		0	0	0	0	0	0	1	0	0	0
Other		0	0	0	0	0	0	1	0	0	0

* generic

Part 3

		Vietnam	Vietnam	Totals
		VietnamNet	Zing	
Number of articles		24	2	
Science %				
	<10%	19	2	333
	10–50%	3	0	55
	50–100%	2	0	39
Who gets quoted (reports)?				
IPCC/UNFCCC		3	0	37
Other int bodies		5	0	25
National organisations		3	0	31
NGOs		0	0	8
Scientists individual		2	0	9
Scientists generic		0	0	22
Sceptics		0	0	1
Other		0	0	1
Who gets quoted (individuals)?				
IPCC/UNFCCC		0	0	18
Other Int Bodies		1	0	19
National organisations or politicians		1	0	40
NGOs		0	0	17
Scientists individual		1	0	25
Sceptics		0	0	1
Other		0	0	1
Reactions to the Copenhagen Accord				
Government Officials		4	0	167
IPCC/UNFCCC		0	0	9
Other int bodies		1	0	10
NGOs		0	0	44
Scientists		0	0	10
Sceptics		0	0	1
Other		0	0	3

Appendix 6: Text of Questionnaire Sent to Journalists

1) What has been your general experience in the last 12 months of dealing with climate scientists?

> Very good
> Good
> OK
> Poor

2) When it has been very good or good, in what way has the relationship with scientists worked well?

> Availability of scientist(s) for interviews
> Ability of scientist(s) to explain the science clearly and succinctly
> Willingness of scientist(s) to comment on the areas you were interested in
> Understanding by the scientist(s) of the needs of journalists (deadlines, top lines, etc)
> Efficient liaising with media officers
> Other (please state):

3) When it has not worked well, what have been the main obstacles to a better relationship with you?

> Lack of availability
> Inability of scientist(s) to explain the science clearly and succinctly
> Reluctance of scientist(s) to comment on the areas you wanted him/her to comment on

Lack of assistance from media officers at university or research centre where scientists work
Other (please state):

4) What would most help you work in the coming months in your relationship with scientist(s)? Please rank in order of importance from 1 to 8, where 1 is the most important:

More media training for scientists
More media training for press officers at universities/research centres
More availability by scientists to speak to the media
More reports by climate scientists on topical issues
More comments from scientists on policy issues, rather than just the science
More scientists who are able to comment on all aspects of climate science and not just their area of expertise
More scientists who are prepared to debate the science with climate sceptics
More presence and availability of scientists at conferences like the COP

5) Which science organisation (university, think tank, research centre, UN body) has dealt best with the media in your experience in recent months?

6) Any other comments you would like to add on any aspect of scientists' engagement with the media in the future?

Appendix 7: Text of Questionnaire Sent to Scientists/Experts

1) What has been your general experience in the last 12 months of dealing with journalists?

> Very good
> Good
> OK
> Poor

2) If your experience has been very good or good, in what way has the relationship with journalists worked well?

> Journalists have a good understanding of the topic
> Journalists have accurately represented my views
> Journalists have not tried to make a 'false' balance between my views and those of climate sceptics
> Journalists have not pushed me to answer questions which are not my area of expertise or about which I did not want to express an opinion.
> Journalists checked with me what they intended to publish/broadcast before publication/broadcast
> Journalists have a good understanding of the importance of peer-reviewed science
> Other (please state):

3) If your experience has been OK or poor, what has been the main reason for it?

Being misquoted or misrepresented, including the editing out of uncertainties and caveats

The sensationalising of my comments

Inaccuracies in the reporting by the journalist

Lack of understanding by journalists of the topic

Insistence on false balance with climate sceptics

Being pushed to answer questions I did not want to answer

Journalists don't have a good understanding of the importance of peer-reviewed science

Other (please state)

4) What, in your view, would most help to improve the work of journalists on climate science in the coming months? Please rank in order of importance from 1 to 10 where 1 is the most important:

More training for general journalists to give them more understanding of climate science

More journalists specialising in climate science

More awareness from journalists of the concepts of risk and uncertainty

More in-depth/reflective longer-format reporting

More reporting based on peer-reviewed science

A less adversarial framing of climate science

More attention to detail and less sensationalising

More careful use of language (like the use of the word 'sceptics')

More inventiveness from journalists on 'making the significant interesting'

Less doom and gloom stories and more positive stories of adaptation or mitigation

5. Could you give what you regard as an excellent example of climate change reporting in the last 12 months?

6. Any comments you would like to add on any aspect of the media's coverage of climate change in the future:

Appendix 8: List of Respondents to Questionnaire

Scientists

Australia

Professor David Karoly, School of Earth Sciences, University of Melbourne
Professor Will Steffen, Australian National University, Canberra

Brazil

Professor Carlos Nobre, National Institute for Space Research (INPE)

China

Dr Zhang Chengyi, Chief Scientist, Laboratory for Climate Change, National Climate Centre, China Meteorological Administration
Professor Yihui Ding, China Meteorological Administration
Professor Wang Shaowu, Department of Atmospheric Sciences, School of Physics, Peking University

Egypt

Samir Tantawi, Climate Change Central Department, Egyptian Bureau for CDM

India

Kushal Pal Singh Yadav, Centre for Science and Environment, Delhi

Italy

Professor Franco Prodi, Director of ISAC-CNR (Institute of Sciences of the Atmosphere and Climate)

Mexico

Dr Victor Magaña, Centro de Ciencias de la Atmósfera, UNAM

Nigeria

Professor Temiloluwa Ologunorisa, Centre for Climate Change and Environmental Research, Osun State University, Osogbo, Nigeria.

Russia

Professor Sergey N. Kirpotin, Vice-Rector for International Affairs, Tomsk State University

United Kingdom

Dr Myles Allen, University of Oxford's Atmospheric, Oceanic and Planetary Physics Department
Dr David Frame, University of Oxford, Smith School of Enterprise and the Environment
Professor Mike Hulme, UEA
Professor Diana Liverman, ECI/University of Oxford and University of Arizona
Professor Mark Maslin, University College London
Dr Mark New, ECI/University of Oxford
Professor Chris Rapley, Science Museum
Dr Saleem ul Huq, IIED

USA

Tom Karl, Director, National Oceanic and Atmospheric Administration (NOAA)
Dr Tom Knutson, NOAA
Dr Jerry Meehl, National Center for Atmospheric Research (NCAR)
Dr Ben Santer, Program for Climate Model Diagnosis and Intercomparison
Dr Kevin Trenberth, NCAR

Vietnam

Professor Truong Quang Hoc, Dept for Climate Change, the Nature and Environment Protection Association
Professor Nguyen Duc Ngu, former director of Vietnam climate agency

Journalists

Australia

Leigh Dayton, *The Australian*
Margot O'Neill, ABC

Brazil

Gustavo Bonato, Canal Rural
Gustavo Faleiros, O Eco

China

Xin Benjian, *People's Daily*
Huan Gongdi, Xinhua
Albert Yue Yuan, *San Lian Life Weekly*

Egypt

Dalia Abdelsalam, *El Ahram Hebdo*

India

Chetan Chauhan, *Hindustan Times*
Pierre Fitter, News X
Joydeep Gupta, PANS

Italy

Mario Porqueddu, *Corriere della Sera*

Mexico

Javier Cruz Mena, Noticias MVS, Canal 22, IMER
Cecilia Rosen, *La Reforma*

Nigeria

Jennifer Igwe, Nigerian Television Authority
Michael Simire, Independent Newspapers

Russia

Ilona Vinogradova, BBC Russian Service

United Kingdom

David Adam, *Guardian*
Richard Black, BBC Online
Tom Clarke, Channel 4 News
Alister Doyle, Reuters
Louise Gray, *Daily Telegraph*
Fiona Harvey, *Financial Times*
Ben Jackson, *Sun*
David Shukman, BBC TV

USA

John Broder, *New York Times*
Margot Roosevelt, *LA Times*

Vietnam

Hoang Quoc Dzung, *Tien Phong Daily*

Acknowledgements

Summoned by Science is the result of such a collective effort that I fear I may inadvertently forget to mention someone, but here is my attempt. A debt of immense gratitude is due to the team of researchers drawn from RISJ journalist fellows and M.Sc. students at Oxford University's ECI and OUCE who gave their time voluntarily to carry out the content analysis. They are Anu Jogesh, Margot O'Neill, Giang Nguyen, Abdalla Hassan, Evelyn Tagbo, Timothy Bouley, Beth Stone, Oksana Vozhdaeva, Leticia Sorg, Chiara Vitali, and Gabriela Jacomella.

Several other RISJ journalist fellows and ECI/OUCE students joined guest speakers and journalists from China, India and Nigeria at a series of events and seminars organised by the RISJ, the ECI/OUCE and the British Council in February 2010 on the reporting of climate change. I have plundered their input into these events for insights, information and analysis.

The British Council's Global Climate Change Programme should be specially thanked for their partnership and assistance with this publication. Their team in China has been particularly helpful. Rebecca Nadin provided very useful background information on the Chinese media and the box on China's coverage in Chapter 4. Yang-Di showed remarkable patience in dealing with a series of enquiries.

The media team at the UNFCCC, and particularly John Hay, has been very helpful in answering queries and very generous in supplying information.

Heike Schroeder at the ECI in Oxford and her colleagues at the LSE and the universities of Lund, Yale, Colorado at Boulder and Columbia helped me to get a better sense of who was at Copenhagen from the academic community.

I am also immensely grateful to the 27 scientists and 27 journalists who miraculously found time to answer the questionnaires featured in Chapter 6.

Mei-Ling McNamara and Cassie Tickell Painter helped to process the enormous amount of data that went into Chapter 3 with stamina and impressive attention to detail.

David Levy and other staff at the RISJ have offered unstinting encouragement.

My wife, Sophia Tickell, and daughters (Maya and Cassie) have once again put up graciously with the unhealthy pressures of meeting deadlines and writing lengthy publications.

Many others have contributed in diverse ways: Fiona Fox, Bob Ward, Mike Shanahan, Paddy Coulter, Fiona Harvey, Catherine Ferrieux, Alex Kirby, Tran le Thuy, Cecilia Rosen, Curtis Brainard, Kamal Kapadia, Juan Arredondo, Mark New, Ben Jackson, David Karoly, David Shukman, Richard Black, Diana Liverman, Susannah Eliott and Risto Kunelius.

As with all endeavours of this nature, the errors of judgement or fact are not theirs but mine.